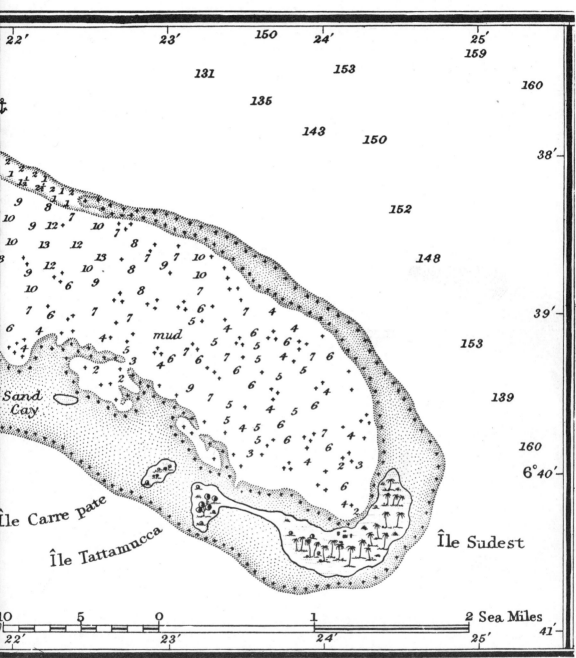

22'   23'   150   24'   25'
159

131   153
160
135
143   150
38'—

152

148
39'—

153

mud
139

Sand
Cay
160
6°40'—

Île Carre pate

Île Tattamucca
Île Sudest

10   5   0   1   2 Sea Miles
22'   23'   24'   25'   41'—

HALF OF PARADISE

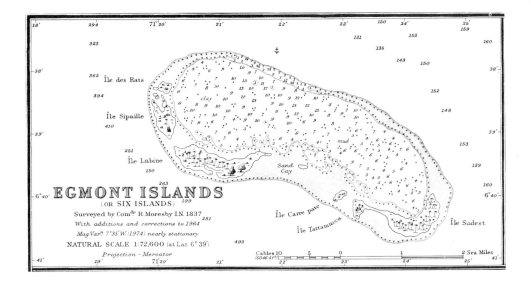

Surveyed by Com.dr R.Moresby I.N. 1837
With additions and corrections to 1964
Mag.Var.n 7°35'W.(1974) nearly stationary
NATURAL SCALE 1:72,600 (at Lat 6°39')
Projection – Mercator

EGMONT ISLANDS

(OR SIX ISLANDS)

Île des Rats

Île Sipaille

Île Lubine

Île Carre pate

Île Tattamucca

Île Sudest

Sand Cay

clay

mud

Cables 10 (6046 4f.t) 5 0 1 2 Sea Miles

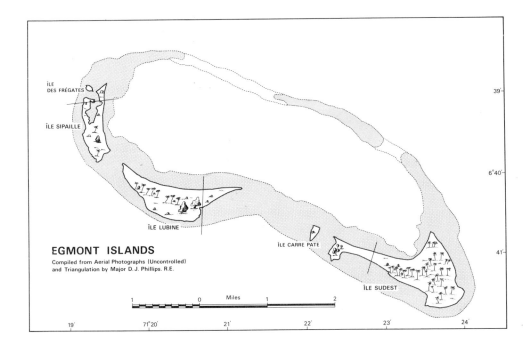

EGMONT ISLANDS

Compiled from Aerial Photographs (Uncontrolled)
and Triangulation by Major D.J. Phillips. R.E.

ÎLE DES FRÉGATES

ÎLE SIPAILLE

ÎLE LUBINE

ÎLE CARRE PATE

ÎLE SUDEST

1 0 Miles 1 2

HALF
OF
PARADISE

David Bellamy

with a Foreword by H. R. H. the Prince of Wales

CASSELL
London

CASSELL LTD.
35 Red Lion Square, London WC1R 4SG
and at Sydney, Auckland, Toronto, Johannesburg,
an affiliate of
Macmillan Publishing Co., Inc.,
New York.

First published 1979

ISBN 0 304 29754 2

To Sula Tue Blake

The land photographs and the figures were provided by Mont
Hirons. Other photographs by the Expeditions' official
photographers.

Printed in Great Britain by
Fletcher & Son Ltd, Norwich

FOREWORD

BY H.R.H. THE PRINCE OF WALES

David Bellamy's account of the two Joint Services Expeditions to the Chagos Archipelago in 1972 and 1975 is fascinating, entertaining and written in a most amusing style – therefore comprehensible to anyone who isn't a biologist, a zoologist or a palaeoastrocartographer. As President of the British Sub-Aqua Club, this account brings back many happy, if amateur, memories of the diving I managed to do while serving in the Royal Navy. I have never been to anywhere as remote or intriguing as the Chagos Archipelago, but I do know how absorbing and awesome it can be to dive among the teeming life of a coral reef.

It is clear that the members of these expeditions have been able to contribute a significant amount of knowledge to the subject of what goes on in, on, under and above the Chagos Archipelago, notwithstanding recurring threats to their lives and limbs from sharks, poisonous shells, moray eels, sting rays, rats, crabs and sand flies, and constant threats to their digestions caused by the consumption of an inordinate amount of sausage. During one 75-day visit the team of divers, sometimes working to 150 feet at night, appear to have become reconciled to the idea of operating with large numbers of sharks peering over their shoulders. Having seen the photograph of the shark and the diver on page 75 I can only say that while I remain fascinated and envious of most of the Expedition's activities, there must have been moments during which I would most certainly have preferred to be competing with the depredations of the rats and crabs on relatively dry land as opposed to investigating coral growths under the water.

Dr. Bellamy and the members of both of these expeditions, and the more recent Joint Services expedition to the Archipelago are to be congratulated on the splendid work they have undertaken, which will no doubt go a long way towards improving man's understanding of the complex and delicate balance of Nature in the relatively little-explored underwater world of the Indian Ocean.

Contents

Introduction:
Getting prepared

Have you ever had one of those really exciting letters – you know, the sort that really do change your life? The only problem is that at the time you probably don't realise just how important it is going to be. I certainly didn't.

Mine came in one of those dull-looking regulation 'Official-Paid' brown envelopes. Among its general greetings and information was a question that was at first sight simple. 'We are planning a diving expedition to a coral atoll. Can you suggest a programme of useful research?'

The letter came from two members of the R.A.F. Diving Club, Squadron Leader Richard Bird (inevitably known as 'Dickie') and Squadron Leader David Rickard, and to cut a long story short we soon got together to discuss details.

In 1969 I had had the honour and good fortune to lead Phase Six of the Royal Society's Expedition to Aldabra, a coral atoll which lies at 46° 20–E and 9° 25–S in the western Indian Ocean some 500 miles from Dar es Salaam on the coast of Africa.

Aldabra is to the biologist one of those now fairytale places as yet but little affected by man, an island where evolution has in isolation gone its own adaptive way, producing a host of unique plants and animals. The Galapagos Islands, which lie almost half a world away from Aldabra, are without doubt the most famous of these living workshops, for it was there in 1835 that Charles Darwin gathered some of

7

the information which led him to formulate the theory of evolution. Aldabra, like the Galapagos, has a large and viable population of Giant Tortoises; it also provides a home for the last remaining population of a flightless bird, the Aldabran Rail, and its flora includes many endemic plants, which means simply that they are found nowhere else.

During the 1960s the future of Aldabra was threatened by proposals to build an air base there. The Royal Society therefore mounted a major scientific expedition to make a detailed survey of the whole atoll. The task of Phase Six was to lay down a baseline study of the living reef front to which the whole atoll owes its existence. Hidden below the surf which constantly washes a coral shore, complex communities of animals and plants work together producing new coral rock which not only protects the island from erosion but expands the reef, creating new land from the sea.

The findings of this expedition may be read in a series of scientific papers. Its exploits are well known to the world of sport diving and, like all worthwhile pieces of research, it posed more questions than it answered. One of the most mystifying of these was the fact that Aldabra appeared to be growing the wrong way round.

Most accounts of reef ecology suggest that they grow best in situations where they are exposed to the turbulence of rough seas. The cogent argument is that the coral animals require oxygen for their life processes and the waves pounding on the reef will stir in an ample supply. In direct contradiction to this, the best areas of living reef were along the most sheltered shores of Aldabra. In fact there was an almost perfect correlation; the more exposed the shore, the less coral growth could be found, the most exposed sections being devoid of living coral.

An explanation was sought in the fact that Aldabra is, at irregular intervals, subject to hurricane force winds and the idea was that perhaps these were too violent to allow the normal pattern of reef growth. I don't know why, but I had never been very happy with the explanation and my mind had often wandered over the map of the Indian Ocean towards those atolls of the Maldive chain which are well outside the hurricane belt.

Dickie and Dave sat amazed as I gushed forth a stream of hermatypic rhetoric ('hermatypic' means reef-forming, and 'rhetoric' in this context means excited talking). They shut me up in mid-gush by saying that if there was all that work to be done, how about coming along and helping to do it? And where was the best place?

You can guess how I felt as I blurted out 'the Chagos Archipelago, and as far as I know no one has as yet ever dived there!'

So it was that the Joint Services Diving Expedition to the Chagos Archipelago came into being and the first jobs to be done were to work out the logistics and pick the team. A steering committee was set up, applications were made through the proper service channels, and we were finally awarded all the right rubber stamps.

As with all Joint Services Expeditions, which are part of the three services programme of arduous training, it was advertised in barracks, ward-rooms and messes throughout the world, from whence applications soon came pouring in.

The main qualifications required of each service member were at least second-class diving standard and/or a minimum of one other useful aptitude. These could range from boat handling through telecommunications and surveying to, as the *Exchange and Mart* so aptly puts it, 'what have you'. All of this took almost two years, during which time David Rickard unfortunately had to drop out as he was posted to other duties. Dickie Bird thus took over as officer in command (O. i/c), with Commander Alan Baldwin, O.B.E., R.N., as deputy leader and diving officer.

While selection of the team was going on the nitty-gritty of expedition planning rolled rapidly into top gear. Equipment had to be requested and cleared from official service stores and from the diving clubs of the three services; transport had to be organised and finance sought from various trust funds (to whom we are more than grateful).

My tasks were less difficult; first to wade through all the scientific literature concerning the ecology of coral reefs and specifically that of Egmont Island, chosen as our objective because of three facts. First, it was part of the Chagos Archipelago, which was never subject to hurricane force winds; second, it was small enough to be adequately surveyed in the two months available and third, the only other scientists to visit it in the past had been the Percy Sladen expedition way back in 1915 and they had spent only a few hours on land. My other task was to find a team (immediately christened *The Scientificos*) who could adequately cover the major range of plants, animals and ecology we were likely to find.

The final team, the Magnificent Twelve plus Five, who eventually gathered in Gan on 29th October 1972 for the last leg of the journey to Egmont was as follows:

Squadron Leader R. (Dickie) Bird,
 Leader
Commander Alan Baldwin, O.B.E.,
 R.N., *Deputy Leader*
Major Don Phillips, R.E., *Survey*
Wing Commander Doug Macleod,
 Surgeon
Lt. Graham Stoddart-Stones,
 Sub-Mariner, *Stores*
Fleet Chief Petty Officer Arty Shaw,
 Dive Engineer
Staff Sergeant Ray Perren, *Camp*
 Engineer Cinematography

Chief Petty Officer Jeff Arnold,
 Dive Engineer
Sergt. Paddy McCauley, *Marine Craft*
Sergeant Ian Purvis, *Communications*
 and Records
Chief Technician Dave Woolf,
 Communications
Corporal Brian Richards, *Photography*
Dave Bellamy, *Ecologist, Botanist*
George Russell, *Algologist*
Mont Hirons, *Ornithologist*
Ted Hinton-Clifton, *Zoologist*
Jim Barnes, *Technician, Photography*

Gan is an R.A.F. station situated on Addu Atoll at the southernmost tip of the Maldive Islands in the Indian Ocean. Flight-wise it is a halfway house from which seven-league-booted jets step their way to and from the Far East. Sea-wise it is the jumping off place for no-where, unless of course, like us, you just happen to be heading south to the Great Chagos Bank. We were, thanks to a lot of very hard work by a lot of people and thanks to R.F.A. (Royal Fleet Auxiliary ship) *Gold Ranger,* on our way.

This is the story of those days that were and ever will be the First Joint Services Underwater Expedition, an expedition which was com-memorated by a special first-day cover, by a more permanent dot on the map of this small earth and by new knowledge relating to the dynamics of the fantastic process of reef growth. It is also the story of the follow-up expedition which returned to the Chagos Archipelago to attempt to resolve some of the questions raised by the study of Egmont. Finally it is the story of the expeditions' members, from the Navy, the Army, the Air Force and the civilian biologists. Each member had his own specialist role to play in the research and each was an integral part in the jigsaw of survival.

The First Half

1.

Count Down

In this overcrowded, underfed, polluted world of the 1970s, we were privileged to stand one foot in paradise. Our task was to put a little-known corner of this earth firmly on the map and while so doing to test our equipment, our organisation and, above all else, ourselves in a variety of situations.

The corner was the Egmont Group of six islands which lie on the south-west edge of the great Chagos Bank. Take a compass and place its point in the centre of a map of the Indian Ocean, and that's just about it. It's odds on that your map doesn't even show it, and if it does then it's certain that the Egmont Group is shown in the wrong place, to be inexact at Latitude 6°39′ south and Longitude 71°22′ east, as surveyed by Commander Moresby, I. N. (Indian Navy) in 1837.

The Chagos Archipelago is a gauntlet of coral atolls and islands with contrasting names, *Peros Banhos, Eagle, Nelson, Danger, Diego Garcia*, each appliquéd by the action and industry of the coral animals on to the pillars of basalt which rise up here from the ocean floor. The Bank itself lies deep below the poorly-charted turbulence of white water like some just lost Atlantis which is sinking into the eternity of a desert sea.

The Indian Ocean is indeed a desert, in the scientific sense: its surface waters are poor in dissolved phosphate and nitrate and therefore support only low levels of production of plant plankton. This thin vegetable soup can in turn only support very low levels of animal

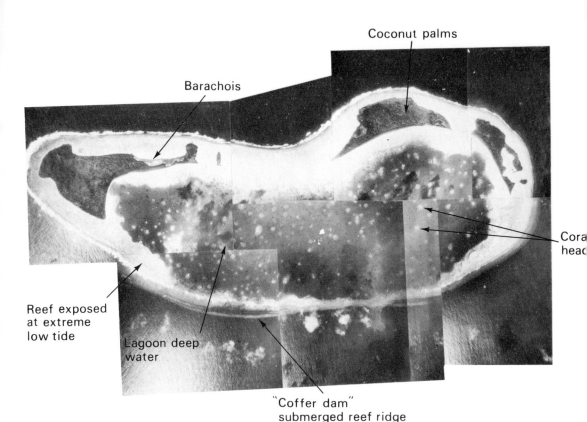

Coconut palms

Barachois

Cora
heac

Reef exposed
at extreme
low tide

Lagoon deep
water

"Coffer dam"
submerged reef ridge

Egmont as seen through the eyes of the RAF
Only five of the six islands described by Captain Moresby in 1832 remain, the rim of
reef rock is only exposed during periods of extreme low tide. Two deep water
channels pierce the reef giving boat access to the lagoon in the sheltered waters of
which 362 coral heads (each one a mini atoll in the making) are growing. The mouth
of each channel appears to be guarded by a rim of hidden rock, what else? — well we
didn't know. This photo mosaic was all the information we had on which to base our
survey.

plankton and hence few fish. The bulk of the enormous daily input of
energy from the sun goes to waste and this ocean supports no large
fishing fleets, while the civilisations which flank its shores are in dire
need of protein to supplement their staple diets.

Each atoll is however a centre of biological activity in this desert
volume, a nucleus of productivity created by the industry of one group
of animals, the reef-building (hermatypic) corals.

The corals are closely related to the sea anemones and jelly fish, both
of which groups are abundant in colder waters. The reef builders are

by contrast only found in tropical oceans, where the average water temperature is above 18°C. Apart from the normal life processes like feeding and reproduction which typify all animals, the reef-building corals possess the ability to extract lime from the salts of the sea and accrete it into intricate and often massive skeletons.

So as the parent land mass slowly sank to become the hidden Chagos Bank, the coral slowly grew upwards, keeping pace with the rate of sinking of the mother platform, the pinnacles of new limestone gigantic stalagmites reaching up from the dark depths into the blue waters of the lighted zone.

One such pinnacle was to be our home and testing ground for seventy-three days. Seventy-three days in which our task was to survey 419 hectares of dry land and the 15 miles of reef which surrounds it and gives Egmont its very existence; seventy-three days of hard work spiced with a taste of paradise and the adventure of survival.

Part of the preparatory training was a hectic but stimulating six days at Fort Bovisand Underwater Centre near Plymouth with a two-day crash survival course at nearby R.A.F. Mountbatten. The highlight of the course was a series of lectures by a Geordie instructor whose delivery and use of visual aids was wonderfully effective, with scale models and even a stuffed crocodile popping up just at the right moment to hammer home a point. We all passed – I quote from the certificate – 'this arduous course with fortitude' and thanks to Flight Sergeant Frank Platts none of us will ever forget the golden rules of survival; *Protection, Location, Water, Food.*

Protection from the immediate hazards of the environment. *Location;* that is letting as many people as possible know where you are. *Water* and *food* need no explanation, except that in these days of taps and supermarkets it can come as a bit of a shock to have to provide your own.

The protection aspect was well covered, with tents, mosquito nets, sun-burn cream and Doc, or to give him his correct handle, Wing Commander Douglas Macleod. There were however some unsuspected hazards – but that would be jumping the story.

2.
The Golden Rules of Survival

The amount of physical effort needed to put and maintain in the field an expedition, the main function of which is to dive from an uninhabited island, is enormous. Seventeen men, 24.5 tons of equipment, three inflatable boats, a choppy sea and an uncharted reef provided the first real problem. To put you in the picture I feel that it is best to include here an extract from the official expedition records set down by Ian Purvis, as they happened.

Extract of Landing from Expedition Official Records by Ian Purvis

Day 1   3rd November, Friday
The expedition members were awakened at 04.30 hrs and started to prepare the three 18 foot inflatables for launching at sunrise, when all of the Egmont Islands would be clearly seen for the first time.

The first party left the *Gold Ranger* at 06.30 hrs in two boats both of which were equipped for a possible enforced stay, carrying enough water and food for two days, should the need arise. One boat crew was to find and mark an entrance through the reef into the lagoon, the other boat to recce the island of *Île Sudest* where it had been planned to site the base camp. The sea state was very rough, and at one stage turned the reef survey boat over, throwing the two-man crew into the water. Fortunately neither Arty Shaw nor Jeff Arnold was hurt, but it did emphasise the fact that great care was going to have to be taken.

The second boat party, consisting of Dicky Bird, 'Doc' Macleod, Alan Baldwin, Don Phillips, Ray Perren and Brian Richards, proceeded to Île Sudest to find a suitable camp site. The first site to be surveyed was where an earlier settlement had been sited. This settlement had been used by the coconut plantation employees from 1809 to 1840, and occasionally up to 1906. It was decided however that this area was not suitable for the expedition's camp site; biting insects, damp, lack of air movement and a general unhealthy feeling about the area made this an unsuitable choice. Further exploration of the island was made, and after careful consideration, it was finally decided to cut and clear an area on the peninsula at the north-east end of the island.

The boat which had been marking the reef entrance returned to the *Gold Ranger* at 08.30 hrs and off-loading of equipment from the ship commenced, the first fully-laden inflatable leaving the *Gold Ranger* at 08.50.

During the day, the three boats ferried supplies and equipment ashore, while at the same time other expedition members were starting to clear an area of bush some 150 feet by 50 feet, which would comprise the camp site. This might not seem to be a large area, but when the heat and the thickness of the trees and undergrowth is taken into consideration, the task then takes on a far harder proposition.

By 16.00 hrs a space large enough to erect a 12 feet by 12 feet tent had been cleared, and while most of the party returned to spend the night aboard the *Gold Ranger*, six members of the expedition remained ashore to be the first to sleep on the island. It was during the night that the expedition members found that they had company – rats! and scorpions.

Returning to the conditions at sea, the captain was not prepared to risk launching the ship's cutter. It had been hoped to use the cutter to help carry some of the heavier equipment ashore, but with the heavy seas and strong winds, the *Gold Ranger* was rolling considerably. Had the cutter been launched, it seems almost certain that it would have been damaged, either during the launching or during the recovery.

Day 2 4th November, Saturday

Another early start by expedition members on board the *Gold Ranger*, and also for those who had spent the night ashore amid the rats, scorpions and many biting insects.

Once again the expedition members spent a very long and hot day transferring supplies ashore from the *Gold Ranger* and clearing the camp site. It was found that the boat journeys were each taking about two hours to complete, that is leaving the beach, loading at the *Gold Ranger* and returning to the beach, so there was ample time between each to stack the equipment under temporary shelters made of palm fronds.

More tents were erected where the ground had been cleared, and the team were working non-stop and very well together.

Included with the stores that were ferried ashore were the 45 gallon drums of fuel, each inflatable carrying six drums on each load, some 2,160 lbs.

Wiring for the camp was commenced, which, in conjunction with a 500 VA generator, would provide lighting for the tents.

In the evening after another day's hard work, some members returned to the *Gold Ranger* to spend the last night with civilisation, and to mark the occasion the crew showed a film specially for the party.

The weather was kind to the expedition as it was the day before, but the sea state, which was choppy with a long swell, made the journeys, with the inflatables fully laden, something of a hazard.

Day 3   5th November, Sunday
The final day unloading the equipment and stores from the *Gold Ranger*. The three air compressors were some of the final pieces of heavy equipment to come ashore, as well as the six large air storage cylinders. There had been an original eight from Gan, but unfortunately two cylinders slipped out of the slings after hitting the rails as the *Gold Ranger* rolled particularly badly, narrowly missing the crew in the boat that was waiting to take the cylinders on board, and dropped into 600 fathoms. This possibility had been foreseen, and as each load came over the rail on the ship's boom, the inflatable was always moored to one side until the load was just above the boat's level, when the crew would reposition themselves underneath the load.

With *Gold Ranger* rolling anything up to 35–40 degrees, the expedi-

Home of rats and scorpions, our chosen camp site
before work started.

tion felt itself lucky to have lost so little and to have suffered only minor injuries. Without doubt this was largely due to the skill of the crew on the winch aboard *Gold Ranger*.

The HF radio set was finally working, and a progress report sent to Gan. This was at 07.30 local time and was transmitted on 7,635 Meg.HZ. At 18.00 hrs local another report was sent to Gan, this time, as the weather was interfering with the reception, via flight watch at R.A.F. Maseriah. From now on, all daily reports, including weather reports, will be sent to Gan, and a progress report will be sent once weekly to the U.K. via Gan.

The accommodation was almost complete, although some members had to sleep in the mess tent for this one evening. During the night, heavy and strong winds had everybody up, lashing down tents and trying to keep beds dry.

So with three boats at work it took 186 trips before the cry rang forth 'come in No. 3 your time is up'. We were in residence, marooned on our coral pinnacle. To celebrate the fact and seeing that it was Guy Fawkes night, Dickie Bird was elected to fire one of our distress rockets. The first failed, the second staggered up to a mere 40 feet and, as *Gold Ranger* sailed away, she flashed out a message of good luck.

If we were going to complete our programme of research we were certainly going to need it.

The heavy gang was led by Fleet Chief Petty Officer Arty Shaw and his mate Chief Petty Officer Jeff Arnold, the latter weighing in at $13\frac{1}{2}$ stone (189 lb), although he did trim down to 12 stone (168 lb) during the expedition. Their main jobs were to keep the air bank full, the camp supplied with electricity, and to service all the diving gear, the three compressors and four generators – no mean task, and, to prove it, in over seventy-five days of residence, 5,800 cu ft of air was consumed by the diving community while under water. This must compare favourably with the amount breathed by the whole party while living on the surface. As if this were not enough, they were also the mainstay of the diving team and between them clocked up 202 hours dive time.

The overall plan of study was laid down by the scientific team and all aspects of the survey both underwater and dry land were regarded as being of equal importance. The feasibility of exactly what could be accomplished each day was entirely in the hands of the Diving Officer and the weather conditions.

Each evening plans would be laid for the next day's work and a final pre-dive briefing allowed changes to be made in relation to the prevailing conditions.

With seventeen expedition members to take their turn, every eighteenth day one person was in part relieved of survey duties to take over watering, cooking and general dogsbodying around the camp. If your day coincided with a particularly good dive, well you can guess it was pretty frustrating, but the jobs had to be done.

The bulk of the survey was however underwater. Transects were selected around the atoll at fifteen points and at each point we needed to find out the shape of the reef front.

The mission of the divers was to dive where no men had been before, fearlessly to seek out and map the main features of the reef front at every point of the compass. At least it was something like that. With a prevailing pattern of south-east winds, and with the nearest land mass in that direction being over a thousand miles away, weather and sea conditions were likely to be the main factor controlling diving. However, living on an atoll which is in fact an island with a hole in the middle, there is one factor in your favour; from whichever quarter the wind blows there is always sheltered water somewhere. It may seem stupid, but the main thing that stopped diving was the rain. There is only one thing worse than sitting in a boat in the pouring rain waiting your turn to dive in the tropics and that is to do it in the Arctic. The chill factor must be borne in mind even 10° south of the equator. We found this especially true, because, in the absence of the fair sex, regulation working dress was starkers, which turned with surprising rapidity into best blues when the sun went in and the wind got up. However, just to make all those temperate sun worshippers a bit intemperate, the sea temperature averaged around 30°C and one afternoon zoomed up to 37°C.

The die was cast and the points around the atoll were for better or worse selected. At each point we needed to find out the shape of the reef front, the depth to which the living coral communities extended and the various sorts of reef-forming communities present.

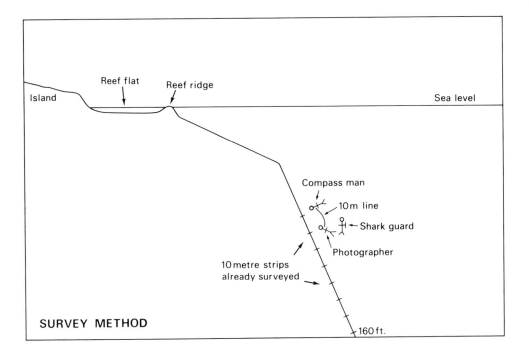

Island | Reef flat | Reef ridge | Sea level
Compass man
10 m line
Shark guard
Photographer
10 metre strips already surveyed

SURVEY METHOD

160 ft.

A community, at least in human terms, is an aggregation of people from many different walks of life who together form a functional unit of society. There are many different forms of human community, fishing, farming, mining, etc., each suited to its location and dependent upon the potential of its own environment. There are also many different scales of community ranging from tiny villages to the great industrial conurbations. Each of these may be linked: for example the food produced in the village community may help to feed industrial workers, who in turn supply the farmers with their tractors. In the same way, in nature, the plants and animals work together in close-knit communities each dependent in some way on the next.

A whole coral atoll may be regarded as a single living community in that if any one part is removed or destroyed the functioning of the other parts will be altered in some way. Within this megastructure there are many separate environments each with their own definable communities. What are they and how are they arranged? These were two of the main questions to be answered.

At each chosen point the reef front had to be carefully surveyed; it sounds easy but underwater there are a number of complications. First and foremost the reef-building communities extend down to about 150 feet (45 m) below low water mark and the longest time we could safely work at this depth was eight minutes. This was not because of the incompetence of our diving teams, but one of the basic facts of diving physiology. Diving at this depth for periods of more than eight minutes means that decompression stops are essential to ensure that the diver does not get an attack of the dreaded bends. (A decompression stop necessitates the whole diving team waiting for a certain length of time at a certain depth before proceeding to the surface. The length and the depth are computed from standard decompression tables.) The only cure for the bends is recompression to the original pressure (depth) followed by slow controlled decompression. With the nearest recompression chamber at least two days away and a sea full of sharks, safety ruled that decompression stops should be kept to an absolute minimum, thus our strict time limit at the bottom of the living reef.

The method of survey to be used was both simple and, we hoped, effective. A survey party consisted of one shark guard, one photographer, a compass man and a board man, the last two joined by a line exactly 10 metres long. The team would dive straight down to the bottom of the living reef, when the board man would record on his underwater note-pad or board the exact depth and the abundance of the main types of corals present at that depth. The photographer would then photograph the board and take a series of pictures of the coral community, the compass man supplementing the photographic and visual record by collecting a piece of each of the corals present. He would then set off along a compass bearing up the reef front to the extremity of the 10 metre line. The board man would follow and the whole process begin again. Meanwhile the guard would gyrate slowly above the working party scanning the shark scene. So the party would progress over the reef front like some weird looper caterpillar up from the bottom of the living reef to the mottled light and surf of the shallows. Twelve transects were to be studied in this way and thus we hoped the first pieces of the jigsaw of information would be put in place.

However, long before the survey was into top gear general trial diving around the atoll brought some interesting facts to light. The reef which surrounds the Egmont Islands is alive around its whole 360°, a gigantic living community 15 miles (25 km) long. There is however a definite gradation of the coral communities. The reef on the sheltered north-west coast is much more alive than that of the south-west of the atoll, which bears the brunt of any storm that can come screaming across thousands of miles of open ocean. Having said that, I should make it clear that the worst storms start around rather than come to the Chagos Archipelago. The Chagos Bank is the brewery of bad weather. So although Egmont can get bad storms it never gets the full brunt of hurricane force winds. In terms of degree of exposure Egmont never gets a full frontal.

Our U-certificate atoll thus yielded its first piece of new information. Like Aldabra, it was growing the wrong way round. In the absence of hurricanes as an explanation, all we could conclude was that Egmont had either never heard of the accepted theory, or it begged to differ, or that the accepted theory was wrong. We also realised that a lot more data would be needed from other atolls before a new theory could be proposed, let alone accepted.

08.00 ZULU

The second golden rule of survival is at first sound a simple one, to locate yourself, that is to let as many people as possible know where you are. Well, the Army knew, the R.A.F. and the Royal Navy knew; so did the families of the seventeen members. Our public relations officer back in the U.K. had also done trojan work and so all the readers of a gaggle of local and national newspapers did, at least during that five-minute period of post-breakfast euphoria. Also, just in case there was anyone who didn't know that we were marooned on the Egmont Islands we had the Woolf. Dave Woolf, apart from being an electronics boffin and a Scout Commissioner, is an amateur radio ham of very high standing and what is more he brought all his gear with him, in five beautifully fitted suitcases. Each night the call would ring out from the radio tent 'VQ, 9DW, VQ, 9DW, VQ, 9DW. Egmont calling'. And there, waiting at the other end of the ether, was the whole world of radio hams all clamouring to talk to us at call sign VQ, 9DW. Some people collect stamps, others train numbers, while amateur radio enthusiasts . . . well, they collect call signs. Each area of the world has its own particular call sign. The central Indian Ocean is VQ, 9DW and as there are very few amateur transmitters in that area, the Woolf was a rarity and in great demand; so each night a great cacophony of voices queued up waiting their turn to record and make contact with the Woolf. Each contact was eventually confirmed by the exchange of cards and in our seventy-one days on the air we not only made contact with King Hussein of Jordan, call sign JY1, but Dave clocked up 370 contacts in a 100 countries. When you consider that it takes a ham with a common call sign such as G, which is England's, over ten years to make his century you will understand just how popular we were.

So just about everyone who is anyone in the amateur radio world knew where we were, the only problem was that we didn't know exactly where we were ourselves. Captain Moresby, I. N., in 1837 put it on his map at one position whereas Captain Sommerville of H.M.S. *Sealark* in 1905 reckoned its position to be some five miles further to the east. As, even with the greatest stretch of the theory of continental drift, this was impossible, it was back to the drawing board in order to find out the atoll's exact location.

This was a joint venture between the Royal Engineers, in the shape and never-to-be-forgotten form of Major Don Phillips, and the Royal Navy, ably represented by Lieutenant Graham Stoddart-Stones, sub-mariner.

Don became the first member of the expedition to earn a nickname which outdid his colleague's double-barrel, it was Major Poncho Macro Chuggles. This was simply due to his obsession with the cover-all khaki rain capes called ponchos and with chuggles. A 'chuggle', to the uninitiated, is a regulation waterbottle made of coarse hessian. These *objets d'art* not only hold water but lose it by evaporation through the sacking and in the process keep the water cool due to the physical phenomenon of the latent heat of evaporation. Drinking from a chuggle is akin to manoeuvring a cross between a Spanish porrón and a horse's nosebag; unfortunately the taste suggests the latter most strongly.

The 'macro' prefix to his nickname refers to his do-it-yourself surveying kit, which arrived in four large crates and one untidy bundle. Together these contained everything from theodolites and subtense spars, through drawing boards and assorted tripods to – most important of all – a flight of 'semi-portable giant umbrellas, surveyors for the use of'. It said so on the packing label. One of these umbrellas well deserved a whole pole-full of campaign medals. It was a thing of engineering perfection, with brass clamps and extension pieces. The canopy itself was white with a rich lining the colour of Renoir's *Les Parapluies*; its crowning glory was a brass ring which could be bulled to perfection and was used for suspending the umbrella above the surveyor. This was a thing of beauty and must have dated back to the Boer War at least. Just to stand under it give you a feeling of being General Smuts himself.

A subtense spar is not, as it may seem, an article of kinky sex apparatus but an instrument looking not unlike a Siamese-twin road sign, which is used for measuring distances. To complete the kit was a star chart, a library book overflowing with mathematical tables and a hand-cranked calculating machine.

However complex the gear may seem the method used for finding out exactly where you are is in essence simple. As all the stars are a very long distance away from the earth, they may be used as fixed reference points against which the rotation of the earth can be measured. Wherever you are, all the stars appear to rise in the east and go down again in the west. Wherever they are on their trajectory, they are at that very moment directly overhead one spot on earth, so if you measure the angle from you to a number of stars at a known time, you will have sufficient information to calculate your exact location. All you need is the gear, a star chart for identifying the stars, a star almanack, a clear night, a good supply of human lubricant, a lot of patience and of course a chronometer accurately checked to ZULU.

How Greenwich Mean Time ever came to be known as ZULU is beyond me, although I am told on dubious authority that it was a decision taken at a meeting of paleoastrocartographers to avoid investigations by the race relations board.

So Chuggles and Graham entered the real estate location business and spent many idyllic nights gazing at the stars, breaking the tropical silence with staccato cries of 'Up Up Up – Now! Oh damn that cloud!' They spent many more appalling days cranking the handle of the calculating machine with plaintive cries of 'Pythagoras', or something like that. It isn't a case of doing it just once but many times, checking each step as you go, because an error of one second in time gives an error of 1,520 feet on the ground, which in the case of Egmont would mean out to sea. So you have to go carefully.

Using a collage of results from stars B Taurus and Andromeda, E Hydra, E Canis Major and a lot more, with no help from Patrick Moore or Gustav Holst and with a lot of hindrance from the moon and a number of pieces of man-made space garbage, they did it.

The true position of the northern point, our camp site on Île Sudest in the Egmont Group is Longitude 71°23′4″ East and Latitude 06°40′44″ South. Captain Moresby had been less than a mile out in his original calculations. That night we slept more at ease in the full knowledge of our exact position.

I don't know whether the rat population ever rejoiced in this knowledge but long before the night of the final triumphant calculations, they were certainly beginning to rejoice in our presence. These rats – the Black or Ship's Rat – were the only other mammal on the atoll, but they were there in their thousands. The faunas of most central oceanic atolls are devoid of mammals, apart from bats which have the advantage of flight to get from place to place. That was true until man started roving about the world, for with him went donkeys, goats, dogs and cats, which were usually introduced on purpose, while the rats went along for the ride. Apart from crabs, the first creature we had seen on landing was a large rat scuttling away and for a while they had kept their distance, but not for long. Forty years on a diet of little but coconuts with coconut milk as a starter had done nothing to their appetites. They soon found that we had brought all sorts of goodies with us to brighten up their gastronomic lives. We were in for trouble.

It Always Rains on Sundays
The third golden rule of survival is to secure an adequate supply of potable water. Six days had passed without rain and three days had

gone since the last of our fresh water imported from Gan had all been used up. We had planned to get water from the closed lakes called Barachois marked on the map but the water in the Serpentine Barachois on Île Sudest had an unmistakable tang of salt, or was it guano, or perhaps rotting bacteria? Whatever it was, it was unmistakable even through strong coffee or saturated lemonade crystals. To be honest gin did make it more or less tolerable especially after the sixth tot, but at that rate our gin would only last another week. Something had to be done, and quick.

A well some five feet deep had been dug with the help of a little bang organised by Arty Shaw. We had followed the coral atoll explorer's handbook to the letter. It said that such a well will yield 'sparkling clear water of high quality'. The water from our well was dark and high, very high, it smelt like a cross between a sixth-form chemistry laboratory and a 100-year-old Chinese egg, being saturated with hydrogen sulphide.

Our first non-diving day was therefore spent alternately pumping the well in an attempt to produce clean water and constructing the Mark I hygienic sand filter, the ingenuity of the gadget surpassing even its capacity for filtration. Water pumped up from the well trickled through a tea chest full of clean white sand to collect in a polythene bucket in the middle of the box. The only problem was that the blackish solution of sulphuretted hydrogen that went in at the top came out as a crystal clear solution of sulphuretted hydrogen at the bottom.

Two cans of beer were now absolute heaven, worth their weight in nutty bars, dubious scientific literature or any other article of island commerce. They were carefully hoarded to be savoured in the cool of the evening to wash the day's ration of salt and hydrogen sulphide (H_2S) from the taste buds. Friday night passed rainless. Most of us dreamed of water, Doc dreamed of a Mark II filter and George Russell for some unknown reason of chocolate cake.

It was Saturday. The scientific programme was to collect 'weirdies' from the lagoon. 'Weirdies' was the collective term used for that cross-section of the animal kingdom which doesn't have backbones, the sub-kingdom Invertebrata – much easier to say weirdies – so the boats were loaded and headed out for the lagoon.

26

Survey team at work, leader, photographer, sample collector and most important of all, shark guard.

Survey team at work and boy was it hot!

The shore party had plenty to do, for the rats were beginning to get cheeky. No longer did they skulk in the shadows but made open sorties into the cookhouse, tents, boatshed, in fact anywhere they wanted to go. The final blow had come that morning when our leader woke up with a large rat sitting on his foot contemplating the aroma of R.A.F. blue cheese. His contemplation came to an abrupt end as the first Chagos rat went into orbit.

They had to go, or at least we had to stop them from coming so easily. The plan was to create a bare expanse right round the camp by burning off all vegetation. So once the first diving party was away ground clearance swung into fiery operation, or it almost did. The fires were hardly alight when we saw a small black cloud which rapidly grew, blotting out the horizon. Neighbouring Île S'apaille soon disappeared into the gloom, as winds gusting up to 20 knots blew Doc into the mess tent, anemometer in hand, shouting 'man the rain traps, to hell with the rats, thirst things thirst!'

Rats were forgotten as the fires went out, the thought of limers (regulation naval lime juice to the uninitiated) *sans* H_2S threw everyone into a frenzy of bucket-washing and catchment erection and very soon the team was ready, standing around the mess tent the brailing of which has been re-lashed to lead the rain into buckets. Cans of beer were wagered on the quantity of precipitation which was to come and the wind waxed stronger. The island of Lubine was lost to view and soon Carré Pate followed suit, and then it happened. The rain cloud divided; Île Sudest was bathed in golden sunshine as less than 0.1 mm of rain (official met. office rain gauge) fell on the island. Four sandy litres of water were actually collected, well diluted by cockroach legs, spiders, leaves and coconut flowers, and an innumerable number of rats sheltered from the shower in our tents. Poetic justice, perhaps, but with Aquarius blatantly absent it was back to the rats and, as the nearest we had to a pied piper was a partially tanned surgeon wing commander with an anemometer, we had to do it the hard way by clearing the forest floor around the camp. Fires raged, the brush burned, coconuts exploded and the rats retreated into the vastness of the plantations.

Operation Weirdies progressed faster than Project Pied Piper as buckets of unclassified organisms of all shapes and sizes arrived on shore for photography, two of each were then preserved for classification and permanent record, the rest returned to the sea, apart from a few choice specimens which were placed in the aquarium for filming and generally oggling at. Paddy McCauley almost committed malacological (malacologists study snails) sacrilege. There before his Irish eyes, vainly trying to bore its way through the bottom of the aquarium, was a four-inch Marlin Spike Auger. As he put it and I am sorry that it cannot be written with a sad Limerick brogue 'good enough to grace even the Pope's shell collection'. The shell now graces the main Egmont reference collection, a fitting record both to the perfection of this great group of the animal kingdom and to the piety of Paddy McCauley, for he found it and dearly wanted it for his own.

Parts of the floor of the lagoon are formed of pure white sand and abound with two kinds of starfish which look like fitting emblems for the plastic age. One is a bright blue ordinary long-armed star which when washed up looks just like a plastic glove. The other is a cushion star growing up to 18 inches across and mottled brown and yellow, making a very good imitation of a leather hassock. These were the first two weirdies to go into the collection, their proper names being *Linckia guildingi* and *Culcita schmideliana*.

So the day passed, the record book got fuller and the diving and ratting teams turned in for their first ratless night's sleep. The now broad open glades beneath the palm leaf canopy, bathed in the yellow wash of moonlight, were swarming with rats. The first Egmont motorway system was open. The newly-fallen coconuts around the base of each palm were like motorway rest houses each surrounded by gaggles of hermit crabs eating and drinking their fill. All we had done was to produce a rat clearway from their retreat in the forest to the heart of the camp, and in they came for their Saturday night on the town. Well, at least we could see them coming – and perhaps they weren't so bad anyway, so live and let live had to become the motto of the evening.

Saturday night had just passed into rat-infested Sunday morning and a gentle breeze stirred the coconut groves, the washing and the bags of specimens hung out to dry. Coconut leaves began to fall, cutting their way like great spade-ended pendulums down through the now surprisingly cool night air. Before the tent's doors could be closed

Not a plastic replica but a real live seastar *Linckia guildingi.*

A slate pencil sea urchin.

A hassock for devout divers? — No a cusion star *Culcita schmideliana.*

the rain was upon the camp and the naked water collectors spewed out into the 8.7 mm of rain which fell in 26 minutes producing 310 precious litres of pure unadulterated water; the water problem was solved.

Baked Beans and Human Bein's

There was really no need to bother about number four on the survival programme. Our food was located, or at least contained in 133 cardboard boxes labelled '*Compo-rations*'. These are, although I hesitate to define the word, designed to provide the average man with a balanced calorific intake. Each cardboard box holds enough for ten men for one day or one man for ten days depending on your level of gastronomic masochism.

Each box was labelled with a letter from A through B, C, D, E, F to G each denoting one variety, one titillating menu for the day; A is for 'orses, C for Cordon Blue and G, Gawd its time to start all over again. Out of the seven types on offer the mainstay for the breakfast in four of them was sausages and beans in tomato sauce and on the other three, beans in tomato sauce without the sausages which are of the pencil-thick light pink straight type with a slit running down their whole length.

Not surprisingly, by the end of the first week everyone was a bit off beans and after two weeks the sausages fell from flavour. Except for one man, the pious Paddy, or to give him his full title Sergeant Patrick McCauley. He thrived on plates heaped with sausages under mountains of, to him, succulent beans. The secret of his gastronomic success he revealed to us one night: 'regard each bean as an individual to be savoured as such'. We all tried very hard to obtain this individual touch but no one else ever managed it, so Paddy flourished and the rest of us reduced both our breakfast intake and our waist lines. To set the records straight the cumulative total of adipose tissue lost by the expedition was 1.4 metres – as measured around waistlines.

Apart from eating individual beans, Paddy's main interest was boats – my apologies, marine craft. We had three of the inflatable variety, each with a 20 hp outboard engine. These are ideal diving platforms, the only problem being that inflatable boats are deflatable and coral

31

reefs are made, at least in part, of nasty sharp corals. So apart from mixing the fuel and keeping the engines in first-class order, patching the boats was Paddy's priority function. 'No boats no survey', was the motto of the marine craft section.

Paddy was however well versed in another marine craft, that of shell collecting. Perhaps it was due to two years' experience on Gan or perhaps it was a touch of the underwater genius, but he had an astonishing insight into the behavioural characteristics of the great family of the molluscs, especially those with the highly cherished shiny type shells such as Cones and Cowries. Following Paddy along the bottom you would see his knife flicker back and forth over the most unpromising looking terrain and every stab would be a winner, a new specimen for the collection. While Paddy had the skill of finding them, Ian Purvis had the follow-up knowledge of what each specimen was.

It sounds easy, collecting snails, a leisurely pastime. Marine snails are different. First of all most of them hide during the day, either buried in the sand or in inaccessible crannies in the rocks. The best time for shell hunting is a moonlit evening, dead calm and, most important of all, with a low tide. Armed with a submersible torch (as all torches are submersible it is best to have one that is waterproof as well), a knife, Paddy and Ian, you are in for a hilarious night among the molluscs. A second difficulty is that some of them can burrow almost as fast as you can and perhaps most awkward of all, some are armed with poison glands and a hefty dart. It is a well known fact that a broadside, rapid fire, from the wrong sort of Cone can prove fatal. So when you grab one it is best to grab the right end.

Finally, once it is caught, the real work begins, because the shell must be cleaned. Molluscs are more or less sedentary creatures, that is they often sit still in one place for a long time and when they move, the majority move quite slowly. A mollusc's home is its castle and he is lumbered with it for life and with the fact that lots of other things especially seaweeds can gain a foothold and grow on his battlements. The mobile, I-grew-it-myself castle thus becomes a mobile hanging garden of easy riders and the growth can soon obscure the shell, providing good camouflage, but it must make it even more unwieldy. So before any collector can be absolutely sure what sort of shell he has found, the overcoat of weed and other even less desirable things must be cleaned off. Just to make the job even harder many of the encrusting seaweeds are made of a substance not unlike concrete, and cleaning is therefore often a slow process of careful chipping.

It is however very exciting, because, as you chip, more and more of the character of the shell is revealed. To an ardent shell enthusiast it is rather like a slow exciting strip show, the climax of which may be a hoarse excited exclamation 'It's a Glory of the Ocean'. Unfortunately it never was. The Glory of the Ocean is one of the rarest and most beautifully marked shells, only a few specimens of which are known, each valued at about $1,500.

What we needed was three specimens of each type of mollusc, two to be kept intact, preserved with the animal inside the shell, the other to be cleaned, the animal removed and the shell only kept. This is the bit that turns off most would-be shell enthusiasts who haven't the stomach for the final part of the job. The shells were hung up in a string bag, as far as possible down wind from the camp and a change in wind direction awaited with trepidation. The assorted molluscs would desiccate and begin to decompose and then the flies moved in to aid the job. The local variety of spiders soon learned what was going on and cashed in on the act by building their webs around the bags, where they lived on a surfeit of flies. Each day Ian and Paddy would walk, lone figures, into the *bundu* to visit their caches, returning only with those that were ready for the final act of dedication. What was left of the meat had to be winkled out with a piece of wire, then a quick wash in the sea, a quick sniff to make sure they had the ring of confidence and, believe you me, everyone could tell the difference.

Once we had got our pristine shining collection, the most important thing was to put it under lock and key. This was not in fear of other members of the expedition but in fear of the hermit crabs. As soon as the shells were clean and the smell had subsided all the hermit crabs gathered round like a gaggle of women at a spring hat sale. In next to no time all the choice specimens had disappeared, each adorning some well-satisfied crab. It makes you wonder how they ever got the name hermit and easy to perhaps understand why the Glory of the Ocean is so rare.

Throughout the expedition Ian and Paddy had this distasteful but rewarding job. The result was a superlative collection of over two hundred different molluscs, the first comprehensive collection ever made from Egmont. Casualties were fortunately few – one hit and a near miss. Ian proved that even the experts can make mistakes by getting a long shot from a Textile Cone which put him in bed for two days, even after treatment with anti-histamines. Doc administered the anti-histamines and a few days later added a Geographic Cone to the collection. Fortunately, he picked it up by the right end because this is one that is capable of giving a histamine broadside, rapid fire.

So we were protected, located, watered and fed, the first Joint Service Underwater Expedition was well dug in and already the data banks were beginning to fill.

3.

"They Don't Like it up'em, Sir!"

The scene was set. We now knew where the main bulk of the under-water work must be concentrated in order to expand our few odd notes into a detailed picture of the reef communities. The first two weeks had gone and the pace of work was to be stepped up. The compressors worked longer hours and the team sweated round the Egmont Air Bank, whose assets were now housed under the shade of a white nylon parachute. From a distance it looked like a weird jellyfish, with Jeff and Arty darting in and out among the guy lines like the tiny fish which find shelter among the shroud of tentacles. The illusion was heightened by the fact that any unauthorised person approaching their sanctuary was immediately driven away.

The line of the main study was drawn, marked on the map and named 'Boulevard de Travail'. In the same way another line was laid down across the poorest part of the reef at the exposed end of the atoll and was labelled for want of a better name 'anti-transect'. It was here that the diving experience of Arty Shaw and Jeff Arnold paid dividends, for their first dive on the exposed sector really put them to the test in a big way. It is true to say that every time the team entered the water any-where around the atoll they were soon accompanied by a squad of medium-range sharks. This time they were surrounded by a great shoal of them, not just the medium-sized jobs but the heavier armoured corps, most of them at least 12 feet long. There was no direct attack, but put yourself in their position faced with all those jaws and you will understand why it took them 23 minutes to position themselves so that their retreat to the boats could be well within the best traditions of the Royal Navy.

All stories about diving, whether fact or fiction, are well laced with sharks. The great fish are always there lurking in the murky waters just beyond the intrepid diver's vision, always hungry, especially for 'Steak bon homme'.

However if you think long and carefully, you will soon find that some of the oft-stated facts about divers and sharks just do not fit. For a start, the average diver is between 5 and 6 feet long and the average shark is between 5 and 15 feet. Even for the big ones which swell up in size when dramatised to 25 feet, an average diver would make a large mouthful. Secondly, the average diver is festooned with neoprene, plastic fins, rubber hoses, a lead weight belt, a metal cylinder or two and sundry bits of harness. Even their most delectable and readily noshable extremities are adorned with glass face plates, depth gauges, wrist watches, knives and collecting bags. Add to this the fact that the average shark has never seen a diver before and at irregular intervals this strange two-legged creature spews out great masses of bubbles and makes muffled noises that sound something like 'come 'ere and look at this'. Certainly it doesn't look much like an enticing meal! Finally, on most reefs where there are a lot of sharks about, there are usually a lot of fish, fish of the right shape, sort and size, and, unless we are dealing with very polluted waters, containing little or nothing in the way of a toxic metal burden.

So the basic hard facts make it odds on that the diver won't get his foot chopped off the first time he dives on the reef and it is consoling to reflect that, if he does, the shark will probably spit the rest of him out.

Nevertheless working on the assumption that not all sharks are conversant with our hypothesis and since, like all good divers, we had seen the film *Blue Water White Death*, we took the necessary precautions. Armament consisted of a bang stick, which is a 5-foot metal pole with a muzzle containing a shellacked ·303 cartridge. Safety-catch off, and one sharp prod should spell doom for the largest shark. The next line of defence was a cunning device like a 3-foot hypodermic syringe filled with compressed air. A sharp prod from the 'Shark Inflator' should

Sharts of the Indian Ocean

Nurse Shark
Ginglymostoma brevicaudatum

Grey Shark
Carcharhinus albimarginatus

Common Hammerhead
Sphyrna zygaena Zygaena malleus Z. mokarran

Black-tip shark
Eulamia spallarzani

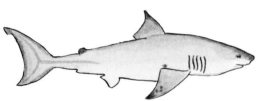

Maneater White shark
Carcharodon carcharias

Black shark Pacific black-tipped shark
Eulamia melanoptera

Sand Shark
Carcharias tricuspidatus Odontaspis tricuspidatus

Black tip shark
Carcharhinus johnsoni C. limbartus C. sorran

Whitetip reef shark
Triaenodon obesus

Negaprion acutidens Carcharias acutidens

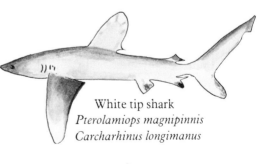

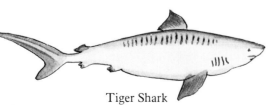

White tip shark
*Pterolamiops magnipinnis
Carcharhinus longimanus*

Tiger Shark
Galeocerda cuvier G. tigrinus G. rayneri Squalus cuvier

Grey Dog Shark
Scolioden palasorrah Carcharias acutus

mainline the shark into a trip to the surface, on a one-way ticket. Apart from these main items of field artillery, small arms varied from pick-axe handles, through broom-sticks, to collecting hammers, all known as 'shark billies'.

Every diving party thus bristled with armaments and each was accompanied by a shark guard whose official task was to ward off inquisitive sharks, but whose job often became guarding the sharks from interfering photographers. Each dive was accompanied by sharks, the record score being Art and Jeff's ±60 at one go. The peculiar thing was that very often the sharks appeared to take little or no notice of the team working away on the bottom, except that they kept close, circling the shark guard who hovered just above the team like some neoprene angel with a rocket back pack. So it went on day by day, the sharks maintaining some interest in the new component of their scene and the diving party maintaining a higher than usual level of adrenalin coursing through their tubes.

Sharks are members of the great group of cartilaginous fish, that is they have soft bones. The group includes the rays and skates, and the gastronomically much maligned Rock Salmon, Dogfish, Huss, or whatever you call it in your neck of the fish and chip shop world, is in fact one of the smallest sharks. The cartilaginous fish are in the evolutionary sense more primitive than their bony cousins, and it is always said that the bony fish are the kings of the sea. However, once underwater with sharks and rays you really begin to understand what perfection is when it comes to riding the currents of the three-dimensional underwater world.

Every man to his allotted job, but every man took his fair share of shark guarding and each had his own particular habits when on guard which made him easily identifiable even in full diving rig from 30 yards away. Some nervously fingered the safety-catch on the bang stick, others practised with the Hawaian sling (the rubber bit on the end). Chuggles slow marched through the water at the 'present arms' and Paddy perched on a rock holding the long stick like some emaciated sitar and played revolutionary songs on it. The leading shark guard was without doubt Commander Alan Baldwin, R.N., thought for a long time to be the first coloured officer in the service. This mistake came about simply because when exposed to more than 10 kilo calories of the sun's energy he turns an instant chocolate brown. Done to a turn, ready for eating he had the exalted rank of chief shark guard added to his post of Diving Officer. The motto of the shark guards soon became 'they don't like it up 'em, sir!'

As the ultimate responsibility of all diving, success or failure, lay with Alan, he had the thankless task of drawing up the lists every day. Now divers are funny people; funny peculiar that is, although I must admit that some of ours were also funny ha, ha. Take a party of divers, especially if they have been trained in frigid British waters, and put them in the tropics and a day with no diving is really bad news. Any all-male expedition is likely to be well laced with four-letter words; ours was no exception. The lists went up every evening and the aptly named mess tent became a mess of pro- and anti-rhetoric, which Alan had to bear on his brown shoulders.

Apart from collecting rainwater, the mess tent was also used for recreation with all variations of card games from clag to chase the lady. With the total absence of money on the island, coupled with the fact that beer was strictly rationed to two small cans per day, betting was carried out in sweeties, each worth ten units, and green vitamin pills each valued at 100. 'I'll see your ten sweeties,' echoed loud and not too clear on most evenings. The recreational highlight was however sand-fly coursing, and this was reserved for still evenings, when there was no wind blowing. On such evenings as soon as the generators were fired a great maelstrom of sand flies would gather around each light bulb. The effect was that if you sat under the light you soon couldn't see what you were doing because of a thick blanket of half-cooked sand flies, whereas further from the lamp you couldn't see anyway. The solution was fiendishly and scientifically simple. The mess tent was about 30 feet long and there were lamps at regular intervals. The course steward would clear the decks by dousing all lights. The light at one end would then be switched on and the clouds would soon gather spiralling round it. That light was then doused and the other exactly 20 feet away would be turned on, the sand flies immediately homing on to it. The whole process was then repeated and the great herd of sand flies galloped back and forth, the field thinning with successive switches, until it was

Land hermit crab with portable beach hut.

Just part of the pristine shell collection, a record for science of things of great beauty.

finally cleared. Betting was on the required number of circuits not on the validity of the reasoning behind the exercise, but it worked, clearing the air for at least five minutes.

Whatever the reason for the demise of the sand flies we were very fortunate when it came to other sorts of insects. All earlier visitors to Egmont had complained bitterly of the misery caused by mosquitos. Having read these accounts, our expedition was well equipped with repellent cream, aerosols and all the accoutrements of anti-mosquito warfare, including the noisiest secret weapon in the business. This consisted of a small fan driven by a high-pitched two-stroke cunning Japanese petrol engine. A mixture of detergent and pyrethrum was fed into the fan and it sprayed out with great force. It was very effective but the only thing that was at all persistent about this whole insecticidal operation was the noise of the engine. We should have known, for when we tried it out on board the supply ship *Gold Ranger* on our way from Gan to Egmont, the Chinese deck crew simply nodded their heads in pity and said that it was the noisiest fan they had ever seen.

However, we didn't need it, for with the base camp situated on the exposed Point d'Etendard, the wind made camp life both a pleasure and more or less mosquito free, not that there were any real mosquitos, only gnats.

So with the equipment we had, and the system of shark guarding, devised by a joint service committee, as long as you remembered to shake out the scorpions, which could be abundant in boots, bedding and clothes, the protection aspect of our survival was 100 per cent. Well, 99 per cent, because despite all precautions we had some sufferers; Dicky and Graham had burnt noses, Ray suffered with his lips, Jim looked like a redskin novice in a monastery and everyone at least temporarily joined the honorary league of the Mandrills with bright pink cheeks, exposed for the first time to the sun.

4.
A Statue
Exceedingly Bare

Dr George Russell comes from Liverpool, to be exact the Department of Botany of the University. He is one of the deservedly famous Liverpool School of 'Seaweedologists' or, to give them their correct title, Algologists.

Unlike the balmy shores of Liverpool Bay, which are dominated, at least where rock outcrops, by large brown seaweeds, the wracks, the kelps and the tangles, the waters of the tropics lack large seaweeds, especially large brown ones. Their place is occupied by the corals which are the main visible features of the shallow inshore waters. The majority of the seaweeds of the tropics are red, small, and many of them are very like the corals themselves, being both encrusting and impregnated with chalk. They were indeed for a long time thought to be corals and were given the name of *Nullipores*, the corals without pores.

The reef ridge, that is the outermost part of the coral atoll that protrudes above water is also the part which bears the brunt of wave and surf action. This hardy ridge is often covered in these coral-like seaweeds. The fact that they are as hard as rock, so that you need to cut them into very thin slices in order to be able to see their structure under the microscope, makes them something of a contemporary biological problem, so many algologists leave them to the real experts.

Even when dealing with the larger type which actually look and feel like seaweeds there are problems. One of the most awkward is the fact that when you are looking at an object which you know is a seaweed you are often looking at only one part of it, that is one phase in a complex life-cycle. The different phases may look very similar or they may look as different as *Nullipores* and *Corals*. Working on your own local splashing ground like Liverpool Bay where much detailed research has been done on the seaweeds, there is a good deal of background knowledge about what belongs to what, and how the life-cycle works, so identification is usually not too difficult. In the tropics, where much less is known about the algae, you may be faced with two objects growing side by side which look entirely different from one another, but are in fact different phases of the same species.

So you see the life of the 'seaweedologist' is not all exotic beach-combing; once the collections have been made, then the real work starts. This, of course, is true of the study of all groups of living organisms and many of the most painstaking naturalists of the past have been amateurs. Today for some unexplained reason this is no longer true, certainly with regard to the study of seaweeds, and this is a pity, because there is still much exciting work to be done even in Liverpool Bay.

Every day our tame seaweed man walked the reef flat dressed in the authentic garb of the famous Liverpool statue which as the local folk-song puts it 'is exceedingly bare'. As the weeks progressed so he donned the colours of the three groups of his favourite plants, first green reflecting the water, then red and finally a wonderful golden brown.

Although at first sight and indeed at second and third sight, the algae appear not to be important members of the reef community, this is untrue. A close look soon shows that just about every square inch which does not contain a living coral polyp is covered with a thick felt of seaweed. Even the surface of the dead coral rock is permeated by threads of living algae, and the coral polyps themselves are dependent upon the seaweeds in a very special way.

The polyps of all reef-building corals contain numerous minute seaweeds each one a single cell but each one capable of doing everything that their larger counterparts can do. Algae, like all plants which contain chlorophyll, convert solar energy into the energy of chemical compounds like sugars and in so doing they use up carbon dioxide and produce oxygen. Ninety-nine point nine per cent of everything else that lives depends on the energy which is stored by the green plants. In the process of getting it they use oxygen and produce carbon dioxide, and that's what makes the living world go round.

The reef-building corals thus have the best of both worlds. With their mass of tentacles the polyps catch small animals which are stupid enough to come within range. They can sit back and digest their catch, which gives them the energy needed for their life processes, producing carbon dioxide as they go. However during the day whenever there is sufficient light the minute seaweeds living in the tissue of the transparent polyps are busy manufacturing sugar, using up the carbon dioxide and producing oxygen, some of which is used by the coral animals.

Just about all the eggheads who work on corals have worked on and/or thought deeply about this biological hook-up. The consensus of opinion seems to be that without their symbiotic seaweeds the coral animals cannot build their skeletons, and no skeletons means no coral rock. There is today little doubt that the coral animals do benefit from the oxygen released during the process of photosynthesis but there is still no conclusive proof that the corals obtain energy directly from their algal partners.

George Russell's main interest however centred on the felt of seaweeds which covered all the non-living part of the reef. What he wanted to know was whether there really are sufficient of them present on the reef flat to keep its waters charged with oxygen throughout the period of low tide. For fifteen days at midday local time George carefully set up his apparatus, and rushed brandishing small bottles into the sea, conducting the waves with a burette. Returning to land with full bottles, he conducted a careful titration to reveal the level of oxygen dissolved in the sea water. His diligence showed that during the day the level of dissolved oxygen was related to the state of the tide. At high tide the turbulence of open ocean water pouring over the reef was saturated with dissolved oxygen. At low tide, with little or no water flowing over the reef front the oxygen content of the water was lower. However a similar series of measurements taken at night showed very low levels of dissolved oxygen during periods of low water proving without doubt the importance of George's seaweed in maintaining the oxygen balance of reef flat. Take away the seaweeds and in places the oxygen balance of the reef-flat community could be in the red, and that could spell real trouble for the fish, molluscs and a myriad of other creatures which make their home on the reef flat.

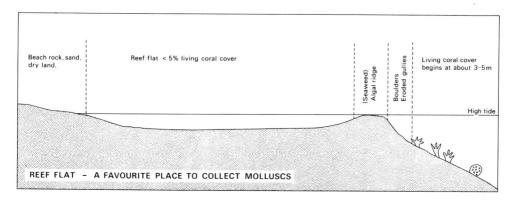

Beach rock, sand, dry land.

Reef flat < 5% living coral cover

(Seaweed) Algal ridge

Boulders

Eroded gullies

Living coral cover begins at about 3–5m

High tide

REEF FLAT – A FAVOURITE PLACE TO COLLECT MOLLUSCS

5.

And More for Afters

Meanwhile back at the survey headquarters the map of the coral reef was becoming more detailed. Dive after dive brought up a bewildering array of corals, and a preliminary look made us begin to feel that Egmont was as rich if not richer in corals than all the other Indian Ocean reef areas surveyed to date. The reef front of Egmont was indeed alive, and alive with a fantastic variety of reef-building corals, let alone all the other animals which lived in every nook and cranny on the reef front. Yet in among all that diversity there was a certain uniformity; a basic pattern could be recognised again and again. The reef front was in fact zoned.

The shallowest zone comprised gigantic coral heads built to withstand the shock of the waves. In this zone work was impossible except on the calmest of days and even then the surge was enough to turn the whole team over and spew them up on the reef flat minus half their equipment and all the samples. Survey of the shallows was thus a long and painful job. Below about 10 feet was a zone of moderate shelter where the dominant forms of coral were delicate branching colonies, some forming intricate enmeshed masses and others large tables standing on a single central leg. Of all the corals these really are the most fantastic things; their edges may be 6 feet from the stem. How they stay upright in the surge even at this depth is anyone's guess but every now and then catastrophes must happen because here and there were great cascades where one of the table corals had broken off and brought

46

the next and the next down like a house of playing cards. In most cases however each one had already started growing a new table branching off from the parent colony so that it was orientated more or less horizontally. In the shade cast by these giant fretworked tables one could gain an insight of what was lying in wait in deeper water.

The next zone was dominated by brain corals, their contoured domes embossed with intricate regular patterning like some ancient mosaic pavement. The surface pattern on one of them was nothing like a brain, being much too regular; it was more like one of those radiators of a very exclusive veteran car. We therefore christened it *Panhard Levasseur* and this name appeared again and again in our transect lists. Only on our return did we find out that this fabulous animal was *Ctenella* until then thought to be one of the rarest of corals, being only known from one other reef.

In the dark blue of water over about 100 feet in depth the reef presented a very different picture, one in which there were no sharp edges or corners, everything was covered by the growth of encrusting coral looking not unlike melted candle wax and everything was a sombre grey blue. Here and there were other colours, rather garish brick reds and fluorescent greens which appeared completely out of place in this grey-blue world.

Below about 100 feet down even in the clear tropical waters there is no red or green light left because it has all been filtered out by the column of water above. Any green and red colours present at this depth must be produced on the spot and certain of the corals have the ability to phosphoresce, proving their existence in this very colourful way. If you switch on an electric light down there, immediately the scene changes as the sphere of the beam of the lamp becomes a riot of every colour imaginable. Better still, wait till night and then use the light at the same depth, when the colours undiluted by the blue backwash of the sunlight appear even more diverse.

A night dive is always a many-splendoured thing; a night dive down in the deepest zone of the reef will never be forgotten. Here the bulk of the corals grow as thin plates protruding from the reef cliff just like toadstools on the side of a tree. The brackets are interspersed with long seawhips and the gorgeous fans of gorgonians some up to 5 feet in length, pink, orange and red, but only in the beam of the artificial light. If they are brought up into shallow water or to the surface the colour remains, but not for long, for in the harsh sunlight they soon die, blacken, become brittle and break up. It is difficult to decide which is best, grey-blue, or all the colours of the rainbow. To me the former is the natural and therefore the best; this is the colour of every diver's dream. In fact the choice need never be made as a flick of the switch can change the scene to your liking.

The night dives brought with them another surprise. Most accounts of coral reefs indicate that the bulk of animal activity takes place during the night, coral polyps all extended, snails rushing about, corals feeding and fish chasing each other. Egmont begged to differ. Everywhere we went during the day many of the coral polyps were out actively feeding, each delicately coloured by the minute seaweeds living inside. We tried to get round it by supposing that it was only a few types of coral which disobeyed the rule, but the more we looked the more we found were feeding in the daytime. To clinch the matter night diving revealed the fact that again about the same number were expanded during the hours of darkness. Diligent diving and recording revealed no definite correlation with any particular factor, light, state of the tide, or to put it bluntly, anything. It almost appeared that the reef community pleased itself, feeding when it felt like it and 'sleeping', if corals do 'sleep', when the need arose. Which is exactly what you might expect anything to do that lived in paradise.

Certainly, if the coral polyps do gain extra energy and oxygen from their symbiotic seaweeds then it would appear to be an inefficient thing to fold up your polyps during the day while the light is on.

Below the zone of the thin bracket corals was the white psychedelic world of sand which stretches down into the blue black abyss of the Indian Ocean. At the 160-foot mark our diving stopped for safety reasons. Below this depth it would appear that there is also insufficient light for the reef-forming corals to grow, and hereby hangs the reason for the zoning. Once below the surface, the light penetrating into the water changes both in quality and intensity. In the bright light of the top few metres, the complex branching colonies which in effect shade themselves can grow. Deeper there would be insufficient light, so that

48

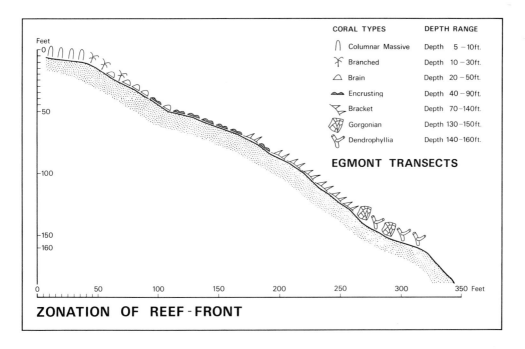

CORAL TYPES		DEPTH RANGE
∩	Columnar Massive	Depth 5 – 10 ft.
⋏	Branched	Depth 10 – 30 ft.
△	Brain	Depth 20 – 50 ft.
⏖	Encrusting	Depth 40 – 90 ft.
⋎	Bracket	Depth 70 – 140 ft.
⊗	Gorgonian	Depth 130 – 150 ft.
⋎	Dendrophyllia	Depth 140 – 160 ft.

EGMONT TRANSECTS

ZONATION OF REEF - FRONT

their shaded parts would be at a disadvantage. Farther down brain corals, encrusting corals and finally, only the thin bracket corals with a large surface area and little or no mass can eke out an existence, at the lower levels.

The same zoning was repeated around the whole atoll, the main differences being the abundance of the corals and the width of each zone, the latter being mainly controlled by the angle of slope of the reef front. Only within the shelter of the lagoon and especially along the lagoon channels was the zoning lost.

Once inside the protective ring of the reef, exposure to weather and wave action is much reduced and in consequence, the bottom of the lagoon consists of sediments, some as fine as china clay and for this reason there is always some turbidity in the water, producing a very different environment.

Whenever high winds made travel around the outside of the reef a hazardous proposition, there was always sheltered water in the lagoon and diving here was always made more exciting by the reduced visibility of the milky water. In these situations anti-shark weapons were

49

reckoned to be almost useless as it was considered that it would all be over before you saw it coming. Gently finning around the base of a large coral head some 250 yards in circumference is a marvellous way to learn about this great reef community. With the sand bottom at about 40 feet, this gave even the air gobblers up to one hour bottom time, whereas most air sippers could last almost twice that time on a single cylinder of air. No pressing problems of decompression meant that on a twin set one could enjoy a whole afternoon as part of the lagoon fraternity.

At first sight the sand was a desert of fantastically repeating shapes, but a closer look revealed great diversity. Meandering lines, each the track of some mollusc browsing its way through the substrata, moon-like sandscapes of depressions and cones, the work of sand-burrowing worms living in the U-shaped tube that connects the two, added their own distinctive variety. The depression is in fact the feeding funnel and a close look shows the tiny cascade of sand and food being drawn down towards the worm's mouth. The mixture then passes through the worm to be thrown out at the other end, clean pure white sand now almost devoid of organic matter. The more stagnant waters of the lagoon are often richer in organic material than the open reef front and without the activity of such animals as the worms this could accumulate on the bottom, resulting in deoxygenation. The living sand is thus an extensive filtration plant, and in this way the whole system is kept pure.

The only fish that make real use of the sandy bottom are the rays, due in part to their ability to camouflage themselves and to lie doggo, part buried, for long periods of time. When there is no danger they move slowly forward like some space age vacuum-cleaner seeking out their food. Rays come in all shapes and sizes and it is just as difficult for a diver to see them as it is for any normal denizen of the reef. A yard of sting ray possesses a formidable long range weapon and it is expedient not to tread on it.

Most of them are however harmless and if you do happen to stand on a big one the only sensation is one of rapid forward acceleration and reverse vertigo. The net result would be landing flat on your back, if it wasn't for the water in between. It may well be a coincidence but that is the best position for viewing the largest of all the rays. The one that has made it to the top in the flat fish world is the great Manta or Devil Ray, which has evolved to feed on plankton. The Manta's camouflage comes in two tones, blue-black when viewed from the top, blending with the dark ocean, and white underneath from wing tip to wing tip, perfect camouflage when viewed against the bright sun.

When the original settlement was built on Egmont the site chosen was the only one where deep water comes close into the lagoon shore, thus making it ideal for loading up the copra ships. There was one place in Settlement Bay quite close to a big coral head where you could almost guarantee the presence of a Manta or two, not big when compared to real giants, but at least boasting an 8-foot finspan. Unfortunately the visibility was usually rather poor in this area but that made a confrontation with the Devil Fish even more surprising.

One evening returning by boat across the lagoon we saw two large Mantas at rest, each gently rocking, its fins alternately breaking the surface. Stopping the engine we drifted in close enough to touch them. They moved slowly away and then started to perform backward loops in apposition to each other, their white bellies coming together in mid loop after which they lay on the surface of the water for a few seconds

EFFECT OF ZONATION WITHIN THE CHANNEL

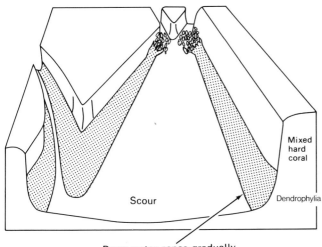

Scour

Mixed hard coral

Dendrophylia

Deep water zones gradually move into shallow water once within the channel

before going through the whole routine again. We watched fascinated for about 20 minutes before disturbing the performance by starting the engine. Only one Manta was however frightened away, the other moved towards the boat and started to roll once more, using the boat as a partner. Finding that this huge black Manta did not respond and roll to show its snow white belly the ray soon moved off back to its mate. Manta Bay thus got its name and although much time was spent underwater camera in hand studying the coral heads in the vicinity, we never did manage to film the ritual of the rays.

Up on the coral head things were very different from the sand; these are castles with battlements, re-entrants, doors and windows, full of shelter and hence packed with life. Each small cave has its own clientele, an octopus brooding over her eggs with a plume of acceptable fish fussing about near the entrance, or a trigger fish guarding its very own territory. However the most constant inmate on these coral castles is the moray eel. Whether it is just man's normal fear of snake-like animals, its somewhat pugnacious attitude, or the voracious appetite and large mouth full of needle sharp teeth that makes most divers frightened of them, I don't know. Once you have overcome the initial abhorrence, they are fascinating things to watch, and any form of meat proffered is sure to be rewarded by a great head appearing from a nearby hole, often too close for comfort. In this way we got rid of an awful lot of the dreaded corned beef from the compo packs.

An afternoon spent around one of these coral castles was always full of surprises. The greatest perhaps was swimming along in the murk and meeting a large shark face to face. I never knew who was the more surprised.

6.
The Main Channel

Atolls come in a range of shapes and sizes and their lagoons in a range of open-ness and enclosed-ness. The Egmont lagoon is open along the whole of its north-eastern rim, at least during periods of high tide. Moresby's map marks a single wide reef channel towards the north end. We had discovered a second one which, though much narrower, was just as deep and was situated almost opposite Boat Bay on Île Sudest. The southern margin of the atoll is a continuous broad ridge of reef rock and sand which dries almost completely during extreme low tides.

Ecologically a lagoon is best regarded as a lake, an area of more or less sheltered water set in the middle of what can be a very rough sea. 'An ideal place in which to live,' unquote.

If a lagoon became completely encircled by dry land, and cut off from the sea, it would soon become stagnant and unfit as a life support system. The life blood of any lagoon pulses through its channels, the ebb carrying away the staler waters and the flood replenishing the basin with cooler oxygen-rich water from beyond the reef.

It is interesting that the one form of life that does not do at all well within the confines of the lagoon is the reef-forming coral. The environmental factors which weigh against their success are complex, a mixture of too much fine sediment in the water, temperatures which could rise above 37°C, which is lethal to most corals, too little oxygen during periods of stagnation and, under certain circumstances, too

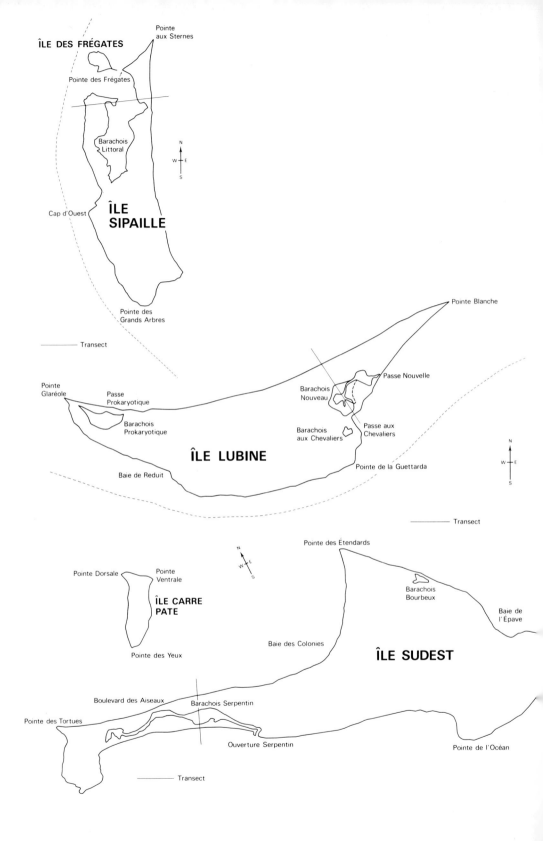

ÎLE DES FRÉGATES

Pointe
aux Sternes

Pointe des Frégates

Barachois
Littoral

N
W — E
S

ÎLE
SIPAILLE

Cap d'Ouest

Pointe des
Grands Arbres

——— Transect

Pointe Blanche

Pointe
Glaréole

Passe
Prokaryotique

Passe Nouvelle

Barachois
Nouveau

Barachois
Prokaryotique

Barachois
aux Chevaliers

Passe aux
Chevaliers

ÎLE LUBINE

Baie de Reduit

Pointe de la Guettarda

N
W — E
S

——— Transect

Pointe des Étendards

N
W — E
S

Pointe Dorsale

Pointe
Ventrale

Barachois
Bourbeux

Baie de
l'Épave

ÎLE CARRE
PATE

Pointe des Yeux

Baie des Colonies

ÎLE SUDEST

Boulevard des Aiseaux

Barachois Serpentin

Pointe des Tortues

Ouverture Serpentin

Pointe de l'Océan

——— Transect

little salt during periods of maximum dilution by heavy rains. Fastidious creatures, aren't they? The strange fact is that if they were not like this then atolls could not exist, for they would soon get filled in by coral growth. If lagoonal conditions are not too extreme, the whole basin will be pockmarked with coral heads, many of which break the surface at extreme low tides. Each head may rise up vertically out of the depth of the lagoon and each may behave like an embryo atoll, the reef-forming corals growing best around their surf-washed margins, while the middle dies away. The Egmont lagoon is resplendent with 362 of these mini-monsters and trans-lagoon transport at low tide had the added spice of a slalom course around these obstacles. Between the coral heads the lagoon floor is covered in deposits which range from coarse ground coral talus to the finest of white clay and it is these deposits which cause the cloudiness of the lagoon's water.

Without doubt the most exciting intra-lagoonal dives were always around the mouths of the channels or along their ravine-like banks, which snake back into the lagoon giving off blind branches at various intervals. Transect 8A went right through the entrance of the main channel and it promised to be an exciting one to study for a start. We had by now ironed most of the bugs out of the echo-sounder and the only problem left was that, like the corals, if it got too hot it went on the blink. The surveyors made available their best umbrella, in the shade of which the echo-sounder worked to perfection, the sonar trace picking out the subsurface features in a very comforting sepia tint on a recorder chart. The first echo run showed a drop away from just inside the mouth of the channel down to a depth of about 60 feet, then up came the bottom again, ridging at about 10 feet below low water mark before it plunged away into the black abyss. We retraced our sepia tone footsteps; no, there it was again, the sharp knife-edged ridge and the drop away on the reef front.

The dive was to take the same form as usual but, as weather conditions were beginning to deteriorate and the water in the channel was in a rough mood, we took extra precautions, two boats covering each dive team.

The visibility was down to a milk-white 30 feet, the anchor rope, taut as a bowstring in the current, disappeared down out of sight. In

On the drop off, the most exciting place in the underwater world.

we went, bunching up below the boat before following the line down to the anchor weight. We were at the base of the ridge on the seaward side where it was fretworked with a sparse growth of living coral. The big fish were there with a vengeance and, perhaps worried by the low visibility, were swimming fast in straight businesslike lines. Eight foot of White Tip shark shot over Jeff's head to disappear in the milk; their acceleration really is fabulous, their whole bodies quiver, strength shooting them forward in effortless motion. Sharks have very special tails called *heterocercal*, which signifies that the bulk of the fin is situated on top of the tail section; this is in marked contrast to the tails of the bony fish, which consist of two more or less equal halves and are called *gephyrocercal*. Whatever they are called they are very efficient organs of propulsion and a shark can make light work of the problems of channel life.

Within the confines of the channel the strict zonation of the reef front breaks down, at least in part. Perhaps it is because all the material in suspension reduces light penetration in such a way that the zoned light environment is missing. Or perhaps it is because at least some of that particulate matter is organic and some of it will be food for the corals. Plenty of food could mean less competition and hence the possibility of a whole range of deep and shallow water forms living together in affluent harmony.

Finning down through the top 30 feet it was easy to understand the breakdown of the zoned light environment, but a real surprise came when we broke through the surface layer of milk down into gin-clear water still with plenty of light left for photography. Our destination was the hundred foot mark just over the lip of the main drop off, where the reef front at this point shot down almost vertically. There are two main problems in working on these cliff-face situations. The first is how to hang on while chipping off the coral. The second is that there are much more interesting things to do than make long lists of the things which grow there. It is in these situations that you can have the real thrill of free diving, proof that you are master of the three-dimensional world. A gentle push off from the cliff and then you can hover in your own free space, adjusting your vertical station simply by breathing out for down and in for up. Great fun, but the sharks could do it much better, so Paddy as shark guard amused himself by shouting at them in broad Irish bubbles. Having finished the work we started back up the cliff as the whole world of fishes seemed to move in to work over the ground we had deserted, searching out the food we had disturbed. What a spectacle – a maelstrom of darting fish set against a deep black-blue background and a living lace curtain of Sea Fans and Whips.

The surface milk had by now churned into a thick cream and the anchor lines were jerking as the boats rode the now choppy channel. Conditions were deteriorating; time to end the dive. Four sharp revs on the motor signalled the other team that it was time for up.

The main channel had yielded some of her secrets, including this peculiar ridge-like structure, an outer lip almost like a coffer dam enclosing a cup of sheltered water. Subsequent survey and inspection of the air photographs confirmed that this ridge did go right across the mouth of the channels. Here was another first for the annals of cor-alology. All we could do at this stage was to wonder why it ever formed.

Manta Ray or Devil fish whatever you call it, it's 14ft of finspan perfection.

Sea fans *(Gorgonia)*, *Dendrophyllia* and fish, just three sorts of animals which find their home on the reef.

Moray eel says welcome for dinner.

Reef shark on patrol, thank goodness he's never read *Jaws*.

7.
No More Than
You Can Chew

Take an unknown reef, circumference 18 miles, twelve divers and a back-up team of five, their task to find out what was there beneath the waves. Given perfect weather, no adverse currents, no trouble from sharks and no illness or accidents among the teams, this gives a maximum of about 800 diving hours. We aimed at a probable total of two-thirds of this and then started to work out the logistics of just how much could we chew, survey wise.

An immediate difficulty is that once under water, even in the perfect conditions of the central Indian Ocean, your visibility is limited to about 25 yards. Imagine sitting beside something 160 feet high and 18 miles long and trying to describe it, let alone working out what it is made of and how it is put together.

The primary survey had sketched out the bare bones and now our task was to add the meat.

First and foremost we now knew that the atoll was growing at what was theoretically the wrong end. The great coral gardens with over 70 per cent cover of living, reef-forming corals are found only along the most sheltered north-west shore. Farther south, both along the east and the west shores, the amount of the reef front actually covered by reef-forming communities gradually diminishes until at the south-eastern tip of the island only small corals are present, covering at the most some 10 per cent of the surface of the reef front. To prove it the whole underwater shape fits the picture. Along the entire length of the most active sector the reef front falls away gently to a depth of 24 feet then drops in an almost vertical cliff down to depths of more than 150 feet, at which point the reef-building communities come to an abrupt end.

Sitting perched on the edge of the cliff you cannot get away from the feeling that you are part of an actively living thing. Everywhere you look there is something going on, coral with the polyps out actually feeding, fish darting in and out of the coral heads, sea whips are whipping and gorgeous coloured parrot fish and assorted sea cucumbers are chomping their way through the sections of dead coral. The whole cliff is so seething with life that you begin to feel that it is moving its ponderous way forward, a feeling which produces instant vertigo. This is an up and down world of weird shapes and truncated vistas.

The other end of the atoll is a very different kettle of fish. The reef cliff is almost a mile from the reef ridge; between these two the reef is planed almost flat by the action of the waves. Diving here is like diving on the open range, a predominantly white world of sand with scattered patches of coral. There is no cover, so you find very few fish of any size except for sharks, and they are there often in ultra abundance, so much so that the area was promptly named shark alley. Immediately the stake boat was on station they were there, big ones, medium-sized ones and a very few small ones, boiling about in a great funnel between the boat and the bottom, as if waiting for the divers.

Imagine, first planning to dive in such a place and secondly sitting on the gunwale of an inflatable boat waiting to drop into this maelstrom of predatory fish. Yet it had to be done, and in achieving it we had the seven most exciting dives of the expedition. The plan of campaign was to photograph strips of the reef front each 10 yards long at the following depths, 15, 50, 80, 100, 120 and 150 feet. Once photographed, pieces of all the different corals, seaweeds, etc. found in consecutive metre squares along the line would be collected for identification.

The first dive was to 150 feet. Down went the anchor weight and up came the sharks, curious about the black shape floating above. Two shark guards joined them, somersaulting backwards through their own bubbles with the dappled sun glinting on the long polished bang sticks.

30 METRES

25 meters

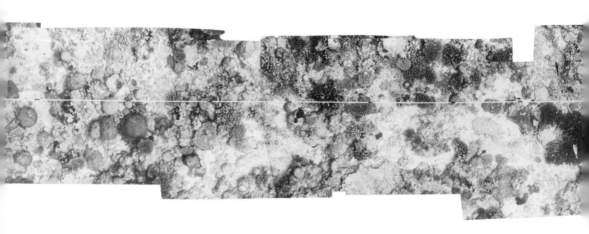

30 metres

23 metres

17 metres

Parts of the phototransect, 360 photographs in all, hard work but worth it the first permanent in depth record of the living reef of Egmont.

The three divers followed and the whole party set off along the anchor line through the clear upper water down towards the outer reef cliff. The shark guards were on full alert facing outwards towards the pack, their lances at the ready. Soon the divers were lost from sight, their presence only evidenced by the plume of silver bubbles like ephemeral jellyfish rising to burst at the surface. Was it our imagination, or were the divers breathing faster than normal? The sharks were certainly still there because two small ones, probably attracted by the glint of light on the ring of face masks peering down from the boat, left the pack and rose quickly to the surface.

On the bottom, all hell was let loose, not because of the sharks but because of the current. The whole team were finning flat out just to maintain station and the precious eight minutes were ticking away. The line was eventually laid, one end fixed to the anchor and other to the only coral present, a large piece of black Dendrophyllia. The photography complete, collection was easy as there was nothing to collect apart from a few scattered sea whips among which the sharks motored, accelerating as they turned with the current. When they had finished collecting, the divers gathered on the line and the sign for going up was given; one decompression stop at 20 feet and one at 10 feet were required. Jim Barnes, who in making the photographic record had probably finned the equivalent of three miles, came slowly up, the *Rollie marine* camera trailing on about 10 feet of line. This was too much for the shark pack, a flashing bait of silver and glass just about bite-sized, an ideal mid-morning snack, so in they came.

Unfortunately long-distance underwater photography is out, but there it was, the original underwater mobile, dangling below us. Boat at top with three masks peering down, 20 feet below the knot of five divers, complete with bubble plumes, bags, hammers, chisels and bang sticks, and some 10 feet below this a small glinting object surrounded by between thirty and forty large sharks. Jim didn't know what to do, reel it in and with it the shark pack, or leave it there and hope that the sharks didn't like the taste. Fortunately they didn't, so once the decompression stops were over – and by all accounts it seemed more like thirty than five minutes – a team of most jubilant divers emerged from the sea and once all the team was clear they reeled in an intact camera, probably the most expensive spinner ever used.

Talk over the supper table that night revolved around one topic, and having watched the action from above, we knew there was no exaggeration of size. Those sharks were big, very big, no need for fisherman-type stories. To top it all Alan had landed a 4-foot barracuda, and fresh barracuda steaks are out of this world, even if you are a diver in paradise. Everyone had wild dreams that night, Jim of dissecting a shark and retrieving a pre-digested camera, film intact. All the divers who had not been on the dive dreamed about their turn tomorrow. Ted Hinton-Clifton reckoned that he had got Sigatura poisoning; well, he did have three helpings of barracuda. One person lay awake thinking and that was Jeff. On the way back from the dive he had seen a mass close to the surface very near the reef edge. Already we had named the area 'Wreck Bay' as there, lying on the reef flat, was a ship's boiler. Was that a coral head or was it . . . ? Arty turned over in the next bed, thrashed at his mosquito net and said, 'Jeff, did you see that it was at least thirty feet long?' Jeff turned over and dreamt of *Shiny*.

All Things Bright and Beautiful
Next morning, the sun shone and the sea was still calm, but a gentle south-easterly was beginning to roll in a long swell. Conditions for diving in Shark Alley couldn't be better. Two teams had been selected and the higher than normal level of adrenalin made even the sausages taste like sausages. The launching was a joyous occasion, but Jeff was unusually quiet and so was Arty in the other boat. With Jeff as coxswain we made rapid progress across the lagoon and out through the reef gap to deep water to void the day's collection of tin cans. Then back in towards the reef, a funny course I suppose, but no one took much notice, except at one point where Jeff was standing at the tiller, eyes searching that area where the breakers begin to heave up and have their being. 'Nasty rock there,' he said. 'We'd better have a look on the way back.' Arty's team went in first, and whether it was Dicky as collector who stayed down too long meticulously working their area, I don't know, but they seemed to take an age. In our boat not only Jeff was getting impatient, we all wanted our dive. At last team No. 1 returned to the surface; the buoy was relaid in 15 metres of water and our turn had come. The eroded white and blue world was ours, and so were the

65

sharks, about fifteen of them gently motoring over the bottom, inquisitive but somewhat worried at our presence. Flash-bulbs exploded,
hammers hammered, coral was carefully put into the bags for transport
to the top and finally, reluctantly we followed it up. As soon as we were
clear of the water Arty's boat disappeared, towards the reef. Jeff was
the only one who knew why and we followed in double quick time. We
arrived with boat No. 1 already anchored in the swell and Arty, mask
on, bubbling in an excited way, arms waving to give some visual impression of what he was seeing. 'It's a big one; all there, engines diesel,
no steam, two shafts, and two . . . great props.' At that he fell over-
board into the heaving water. After he had hauled himself back over
the side, a plan of campaign was soon laid and the sea spouted with
eleven snorkels.

A wreck under water is a glorious thing. But when it is in the warm
shallow water of a coral reef, it is indescribable. On the bottom was a
great ship, split open along its length like a great herring ready for
gutting. The two engines were lying on their sides and the cogs of the
reduction gear had sheared clean from the drive-shafts. The pair of
shafts were still dead straight as if ready for action, their ends firm in
the A frames and terminated by the screws, one in perfect condition
without a scratch, the other deeply scored, with the tips of the blades
worn away, probably during the last desperate manoeuvre to avoid the
reef. Everywhere parts of this once living ship lay, some clean and still
shining, others heavily encrusted with coral and weed. As Arty had
said, it's a big one and it's all there, and what was more, hovering
above the sharp end you could see clear to the stern except for the fish.
In fact with a snorkel and a face mask you could have seen the whole
ship if it wasn't for the fishes in between.

The whole wreck was boiling with fish of all shapes and colours and
all of them were large. There were shoals of all the common ones we
were used to diving with, Caranx, King Fish, Red Snapper, Moorish
Idols, long thin Garfish and short fat Grouper, ranging from a couple
of feet to those that looked about twice the size of a dustbin. We almost
forgot about the sharks, and Dicky Bird was seen to swim up to a 6-
foot Reef, leisurely take its portrait and swim back down to the wreck.
You could in fact always tell exactly where the sharks were, as swathes

appeared in the great walls of fish, the sharks swimming through the clearway.

More facts began to fit together, facts which told us more about the life of the great reef. The most likely place for a ship to be wrecked would be the most exposed end of the atoll, the gently shelving reef ridge giving no warning of the danger ahead. The wreckage, although a fitting epitaph to the rigours of wind and waves, was itself providing safe shelter in what had been a white wilderness of rock and sand. The wreck had in fact produced an artificial reef constantly supplied with waters, rich in oxygen and dissolved nutrients and hence in food. The potential of this haven is now exploited by a phenomenal community of fish.

New information, but also new questions to be answered and not even the most dedicated of scientists could help wondering just what the ship was, when she went down and why. In all the research we had done into the Egmont Islands we had found no mention of her demise.

Next day was Sunday, officially make and mend day, but every Sunday dives were organised and by evening the row of specimens to add to the collection was almost as long as that from a normal working day. Wreck diving was to be the order of the next make and mend day and plans were well laid. Many of the team had been on archaeological dives before. Arty, Jeff and Alan had worked on the *Royal Griffon* soon after the Spanish Armada galleon was found off Fair Isle in 1970. Practically all the team had worked on the excavation of the *Mary Rose* at some time or another, while Brian Richards had gained his under-water photomosaic knowhow in preparing photomosaics of wrecks from Scotland to the Azores. The hunt for the identification of our wreck was thus on.

What could be more perfect, 06.00 hours on a fine make and mend morning spiced with the promise of surveying an unknown wreck? The formalities of breakfast were informalised in the usual way and by 06.30, the lagoon was heaving with boats and the flotilla was off, out through the main pass and south, skirting close to the reef edge full throttle towards Wreck Point. The day was ideal with bright sun and a prevailing onshore wind that was rolling the waves in towards the reef. Three anchor weights plummeted on short lines down to lie close to the two large engines; kit on, final checks and in we went. There was the wreck split open for survey and the engine blocks were just beginning to break water, as it was nearing low tide.

Perfect conditions – well, they appeared to be, until we started the survey. Remember the location. I certainly will never forget it. We were slap bang in the middle of a million square miles of ocean, diving on the most exposed end of a tiny atoll in a 10-foot swell. Below water that swell is translated into a rapidly reciprocating lateral surge and you the diver surge with it. If you close your eyes under water you have very little sensation of movement, but as soon as you open them, you find your points of reference are moving backwards and forwards at a rate of knots. Ouch! no, you are moving and the wreck is standing still. It's sharp and it hurts; and it's all happening very quickly.

A couple of extra pounds of lead threaded on to your weight belt do help a bit, but the secret of success is to know exactly what you have to do and once down in among the wreckage to let nothing distract you from the task in hand.

My first job, working with Ian Purvis, was to measure the distance from the reduction gear on the engines to the sharp end, which I am assured by all our naval members should be called the bow. I had one end of the tape and for a split second managed to make fast to the big bronze gear wheel, which then proceeded to move offstage left, returning with equal rapidity. This time I got a real good hold, my back against the gear and my feet wedged against the propellor-shaft. Ian signalled O.K.; I replied and off he went finning flat out and tacking his way through the shoals of fish. Jammed there, holding on for grim death, I got great comfort from the fact that not only we humans were being knocked about by the surge, but the fish seemed to be having just as much of a rough time.

My mind had wandered from the job; I shot sideways, then back underneath the propellor-shaft, the tape having become hitched on an engine bolt. I regained station, anchored firmly and reeled in, a tug and the tape came loose as I breathed a bubble plume of relief.

Our second fix, if that is the right word, was in a narrow gully paved with ship's plates in various states of encrustation. Plenty to hang on to and I needed it because the gully was channelling the surge, 'blowing' all the fish along like coloured peas in a water-driven pea-shooter. Ian disappeared in a cloud of Caranx while I made as fast as I could and settled down to wait for the come on signal. All of a sudden the pattern of fish behaviour in the gully changed. Instead of reciprocating back and forth they were all moving in a very businesslike, 'let's get the hell out of here' way. Even the Needlefish were swimming horizontally rather than bouncing along nose down in their usual formation. Looking up gully I soon saw the reason for all this hurried fish exodus in the shape of a large Reef shark which was alternately accelerating and decelerating with the surge. An ill-timed lunge with my shark billy coincided with an extra large surge of water, so instead of the shark's swimming away as they usually did, it came on. I can remember the whole thing as if in slow motion; clout went my pick-axe handle; on came the shark. Thinks: 'I wonder what bit it will bite?' So I proffered my left hand, taking a firmer grip on the billy with my right. This was probably the stupidest thing I did, because it necessitated leaving go of whatever it was I was holding. I did a quick backward somersault and landed about 20 feet further up the gully. The shark had gone, but its pet Remora had stayed on to inspect this funny shark-clouting object. Finding some shelter on the lee of my prostrate now re-anchored form he 'sniffed' along my leg and must have decided that I wasn't nice to know because he soon shot off after his big brother.

During this episode, which must have lasted all of five seconds, I had completely forgotten the tape, which had fortunately billowed up into a great arc above my head. I re-anchored, reeled in and pretended that I had been in charge all the time. The third leg (an unfortunate term after that which had just passed) of our task took us into the comparative shelter of the bow plates, between which two gigantic piles of rusted concretion marked the position of the anchor lockers. The total distance as measured and as the Reef shark swims was 86 metres and it had taken twenty-eight minutes' worth of precious air to find that out.

We were however not alone in our difficulties; the other teams were having it just as bad. The scene amidships was medieval. Chuggles was writhing on the bottom; the board on which he was trying to sketch the engines was acting more like an aqua plane than a writing-pad. Above

69

him Graham and Paddy each armed with a candy-striped ranging pole were riding the surge, dodging round all the superstructure like two sub-aqua knights in a joust.

The work was well under way when there was an explosion just left of the main shaft. The explosion was our leader; he had just found the ship's bell. Jubilation from all. That evening our signal back to base included a question, 'Request information regarding the *El Maren* 1920', for that was the inscription which gradually came to light as the ship's bell was bulled back to the light of 1972. The answer came several days later. *El Maren*, a Swedish ship launched 1920, gross tonnage 5,783 tons, lost on her maiden voyage while returning from Australia to the U.S. with a general cargo of wool and grain.

The survey of the wreck fills a number of very happy pages in the dive log and from our findings there seems little doubt that anchors were stowed and engines were ahead at the time of the collision. There seems also little doubt that if her course had been just a few points to starboard she would have lived to ride another tide. We all spent a lot of time wondering about the fate of the crew for it wasn't until we returned to the U.K. that we found that everyone had escaped and returned home safe via Peros Banhos. We erected a cairn of slabs of coral rock on the point opposite the position of the wreck. It bears the name *El Maren* and the ship's bell was rung to welcome the New Year in. On that occasion the Fleet Chief's Toast was, 'the Crew of the *El Maren*'.

8.

Green Fingers

One of the most exciting things about visiting a new place is that it always screams out a string of stimulating questions. So it was with Egmont. The trouble was that most of the most important questions, and for that matter the answers, were way down below us. Just what were we sitting on? What was the exact history of the platform upon which the corals had and were continuing to do their own particular thing?

The now accepted theory of continental drift at least in part provides us with the basis of an answer. It has been suggested that as the sub-continent of India moved northwards away from Africa it left in its ponderous wake a trail of volcanism, of lava pouring forth from the bed of the sea. The lava on which the Chagos Archipelago so comfortably sits was probably formed in the Cretaceous period, that is around 130 million years ago. The interesting thing to know would be how close to the surface of the sea it came because today it is hidden under between one and two miles of coral rock. It would seem safe to conclude that at one time the basalts were much closer to the surface, a platform extending well up into the zone illuminated by the light of the sun. Since that time it must have been slowly sinking down, the industry of the coral communities alone keeping its head almost above water. Almost but not quite, for the simple reason that coral cannot grow above high water mark.

There is however no doubt that only 20,000 years ago much more of

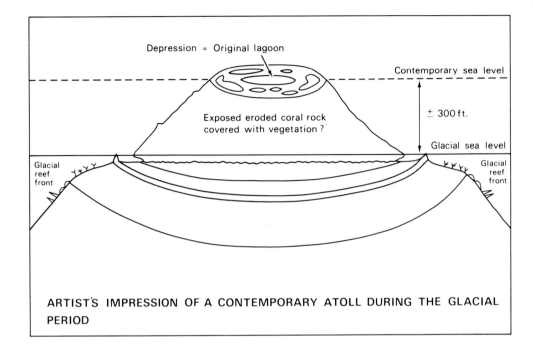

Depression = Original lagoon

Contemporary sea level

Exposed eroded coral rock
covered with vegetation ?

± 300 ft.

Glacial sea level

Glacial
reef
front

Glacial
reef
front

ARTIST'S IMPRESSION OF A CONTEMPORARY ATOLL DURING THE GLACIAL
PERIOD

the Chagos Bank did protrude from the sea. The reason is simple; at
that time the northern hemisphere was still in the grip of the fourth
great ice age, the ice-cap of which reached in Britain as far south as
north London and there were subsidiary caps on the mountain ranges
far south of this. Now all that ice must have come from somewhere
and, as ice is solid water, it must have come out of the sea. In consequence of all that water loss the average world sea level went down
by about 100 metres. The ice age lasted a mere million years and
during that time there must have been many high rise islands sticking
out of the Indian Ocean each with its own reefs fringing its shores. The
end of the ice age meant the return of the ice water into the world's
oceans and as it didn't happen all at once the oceans must have
gradually filled up to their present level. The process is in fact still
going on as the so-called permanent ice-caps and glaciers, all that
remain of the ice-sheets of the past, are still gradually melting. The
bulk of the Chagos Bank was thus re-flooded and the reefs which could
grow upwards did so, keeping as it were their heads just below the

surface of the rising waters.

So Egmont must have come into being as a platform under the waves and through the agency of time and the industry of coral animals it was built up to form a platform which is just below the contemporary surface of the sea, a platform pounded by waves that are whipped up by the trade winds blowing across the Indian Ocean. These are two dynamic systems the interplay of which keeps Egmont high and dry, the platform maintaining its tenuous existence balanced precariously between growth and erosion. The growth of the coral animals adds new rock to the platform, while erosion by the waves and the wind removes great masses of dead coral rock and sand, throwing it up into the shallows where it collects, building on the platform and producing real dry land. Thus any part of a reef or atoll which is dry land must be the result of these secondary processes of atoll formation.

Wherever there is dry land, a supply of readily erodable rock and an inshore wind, there are sand dunes the world over, some along the east coast of Australia attaining a height of nearly 1,000 feet (over 300 metres). Dunes however are not built by sand alone. Sand deposited all by itself would soon blow away. Stabilisation depends on the growth of plants.

Sand dunes are very similar the world over, for the main stabilising agents are a group of grasses which can thrive in the harsh conditions. The dunes of Egmont are different. At their biggest they rise to a magnificent height of 6 feet even though the main sand binder is not a grass but a tall shrub which rejoices in the name of *Scaevola taccada*. Whatever it sounds like, it looks like an underdeveloped rhododendron with bright green leaves and small sweet-scented white flowers. Its habitat is sand and what is more it doesn't appear to mind having its leading shoots dipped in the sea. Coupled with these attributes is the fact that wherever the stems touch the ground they can root, binding the sand around them. In this way the bush and the dunes gradually advance, creating new land. If you own an island or even a bit of an island and you wish to increase your holding just invest in a few Scaevola seeds and you will be able to stand with your heir and with a sweeping gesture out to sea say 'one day all that may be yours'. So the Scaevola hedge holds the island together, and it needs some holding

73

because much of the main bulk of each islet is below sea level.

Behind the Scaevola hedge are the now disused coconut plantations, the floors of which are heaped high with the great cast leaves and piles of rotting coconuts. They may be lost to the copra trade but wherever light penetrates the dense canopy of leaves each of which may be over 15 feet long, each rotting husk becomes a microcosm of green life covered with spreading patches of liverwort and moss. Even where no light reaches down to ground level the rich energy source in each nut does not go to waste. The delicate weft of threads which prelude the frail bodies of tiny toadstools and bracket fungi, orange, yellow and white add their own diversity of colour to the sombre brown of decay. The most surprising find in this line of life was a bright orange cup fungus looking like a piece of discarded orange peel that was living unattached inside a broken coconut presumably discarded by some well-fed crab.

Among the once ordered ranks of palms are remnants of what is probably the original broad-leaved forest, plots in which time has stood still and man has come and gone. In fact along much of the seaward side of the islands the Copra planters, knowing the problems of erosion, left narrow tracts of broad-leaved forest as an extra living barrier against the forces of erosion. Groves of Takamaka, their gnarled white-barked boles and weft of roots which crisscross the ground in a serpentine mass, are the most striking. Everything about this tree is beautiful. In general shape it is not unlike the best tradition of English oak and indeed, like its temperate counterpart, its wood was and in fact still is used for the construction of pirogues, the all-purpose boat of the Indian Ocean. Each leaf is textured like the green velvet of an expensive smoking jacket and is figured with at least 200 veins running parallel to each other and to the edge of the leaf. The flowers are perhaps the crowning glory, sprays of wax white blooms, each centred with clustered yellow anthers, the whole filling the still evening air with a warm fragrance of – there can be no other name for it – Takamaka.

Preference in anything is always a very personal matter, so it is difficult to say that of Egmont's trees the Takamaka is the best. In my estimation the rose tree certainly comes up to the same high stan-

Shark at work, goody or baddy? You never really know.

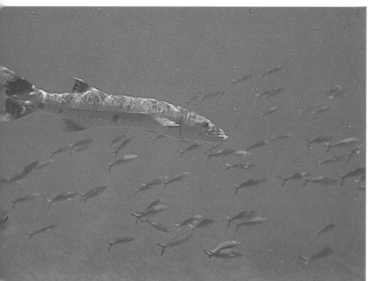

Barracuda, top of the predator school.

You can identify them by their teeth, if you can get a real good look.

A 'Rose' by any other name could smell no sweeter *Barringtonia asiatica.*

dard. It is a giant of a tree with a multiple bole which can be over 12 feet in circumference. The spreading branches bear great clusters of leaves which look not unlike open cos-lettuce. Groups of green buds terminate the leaf branches and on consecutive mornings one bud in each group opens rapidly to reveal four oblong white petals enclosing a mass of hundreds of flamingo pink filaments each of which end in a rose-pink anther. Like most things of great beauty they don't last long, falling as soon as the heat of the morning strikes up from the white sand. Soon the ground is covered with the large but delicate pink masses and the whole island for as much as an acre is heavy with their almost sickly rich scent. This is not however the end of the story of these ephemeral flowers. Left on the tree the fat green ovaries, each terminated by a long beak-like style, soon begin their final transformation which is in its own way as rapid as the process of flowering. The ovary enlarges to produce a fruit about the size and shape of a square eating apple, which rapidly turns brown and eventually falls with a resounding thud down on to the ground.

Long before we discovered any rose trees on the island we had regularly found these fruits, each with a square fibrous outer husk, washed up among the flotsam of coconuts. Each one was seized upon and hoarded as an example of an aberrant coconut. It was not until about five of them had become treasured possessions, that we penetrated the jungle to the west of the camp, following our noses to make our first sighting of the provider of square coconuts, a large specimen of *Barringtonia asiatica.* Another clue to the presence of the rose tree had also gone unheeded; Mont Hirons' ultra-violet light trap attracted and caught Humming Bird Hawk moths with monotonous regularity, the best catch being twenty-seven in one night. The regular appearance of these large insects showed that there must be a breeding colony on the island, and that they were not just strays blown to the atoll from elsewhere. To catch them only at night was itself interesting because in Europe the Humming Bird Hawk is out and about feeding during the daytime, hovering exactly like a humming bird drinking the nectar from the flowers. The facts began to fit. The moths and the exotic flowers both come out at night, the moths feed from the flowers and in so doing pollinate them. Final proof came, if any was needed, with the examination of a captured moth, which was covered in *Barringtonia* pollen. The efficacy of the process of pollination was evidenced by the number of fat fruits which fell to the earth each day so much so that the area beneath the canopy of the parent tree was an impenetrable jungle of young trees in various stages of development ranging from the first two seed leaves to thin saplings straight and striving up towards the light. This is the main problem of producing a large heavy fruit for although it can store a lot of food, how can it be dispersed? Light fruits can be blown about, small prickly ones are transported in the fur of animals, but there are difficulties if your fruit weighs more than a few grams. The fruit of the rose tree, like the coconut, is in fact designed for water transport, which is O.K. if you happen to grow in the right place, on the edge of the sea, but on an island which is gradually expanding, such a plant is liable to be left high and dry, at least dispersal wise.

Findlay who visited the Chagos Archipelago in 1860 made the following general statement about the vegetation of the islands. 'On nearly every part of the islands grow at intervals great clumps of gigantic trees, the Bois Mapou or rose tree which attains an enormous height even to 200 feet (60 m).' There seems little doubt *Barringtonia asiatica* has been sorting out its problems of dispersal in the Chagos long before man got to the atoll.

There also seems little doubt that there was not much in the way of natural vegetation of Egmont which was of direct use to man, except the wood of the great trees for boatbuilding and of their lesser kin for

77

Macroglossum corythus

Hippotion velox

Hemianx ephippiger

Periplaneta americana

Aëdes (Stegomyia) albopictus

Junonia villida chagoensis

Agrius convolvuli

Hypolimnas missipus — male

Oryctes rhinoceros

Hypolimnas missipus — female

fuel. Man brought the coconut and founded a quasi-economy based on this useful plant which is said to have seventy-four uses, sixty-two of which make you drunk. Copra makes coconut oil, the fibres of the husk go for matting, the shell itself produces a charcoal and a flame hot enough to fire pottery, while leaves are used for woven roofs and all sorts of basketwork. The milk gives a variety of beverages from cool to very hot alcohol-wise. It is probably the alcohol *sensu stricto* that makes them all exciting drinking, but it is the other organic compounds, by-products of the fermentation process, which probably produce the never-to-be-forgotten tastes or hangovers. In the same way ferment-able juices may be tapped from just about any part of the plant, roots, trunk, but best of all from the central petioles of the leaves.

The most exotic food produced from the coconut is the central mass of developing leaves themselves which are eaten under the name of millionaire's salad, the name reflecting the value of the palm to the island's economy and the fact that once the salad has been prepared the palm is dead.

With the palm man brought other plants some like Paw Paw for food, the Flame of the Forest for decoration and a host of adventive weeds which came in with true pioneering vigour and rampaged over the islands. All members of the natural vegetation must have got there under their own steam, their fruits and seeds either floating or carried on driftwood or on the feet or feathers of migratory birds. It must have been a very long process but in time the white island skeleton of coral rock and sand was gradually transformed into a dense pattern of green shade. In the same way the land animals must have gradually colonised the now green platform. Again it is easy to understand how the birds and perhaps flying insects made the long sea trip, but did all the rest like geckos, earthworms, millipedes, scorpions, etc. wait and hitch a ride with man?

You know we take an awful lot for granted on our mainland homes and one of these is earthworms. If it were not for these elastic animals and the whole host of insects and other small creatures which live hidden from the light of day beneath our feet there would be no such thing as fertile soil. It is their tireless action which churns and sifts the soil, bringing new supplies of minerals into cycle and ensuring the penetration of oxygen and water and the release of carbon dioxide from what otherwise would be a stagnant soil. There is nothing which could merit the term soil on the Egmont's 418 hectares, yet forty-eight dif-ferent sorts of plants thrive on the sand and coral talus: in time as a true soil develops the potential of such a system could be enormous. The ingredients are there; all that is required is time.

9.

Mont's Motel, or One Good Tern

Egmont is a long long way from nowhere or to anywhere depending from which way you look at it. Although in our days of pre-enlightenment B.C., that is 'Before Chuggles', we humans didn't know exactly where it was, many of the birds of both the northern and southern hemispheres must have known for a long time, since they use it as a stopover in their long migratory runs.

In 1882 a coaling station was instituted at Diego Garcia, a large atoll some 40 miles south-east of Egmont. Its function was to refuel the ships which plied the trade routes between Europe and Australia. Birds like the Turnstone had probably pioneered this route many thousands of years before, the atolls of the Chagos offering a place of rest and an abundance of stones to be turned for food.

Whatever sort of bird you are, location is just the first of many problems of living even on a tropical paradise and the longer your stay the more are the problems. It was Mont Hirons' job, not only to study these problems but also to produce a master list of all birds using the Egmont Motel and the territorial waters of the British Indian Ocean Territories.

If you know your birds as well as Mont Hirons does, the second part of the task is simple, a walk around the island (preferably without a rabble of loud-mouthed beachcombers), binoculars at the ready is all that is required. It was in fact made almost too easy because the major-ity of the birds showed little if any fear of man. Migrants like the

Swallow and the Swift, knowing probably all too well the bad habits of *Homo sapiens*, kept their distance. The locals like the Fairy, the Noddy terns and the Plovers found us objects of great interest and came in to get a real close look. The nearest encounter was a juvenile Brown Booby bird who mistook the khaki hat covering Arty Shaw's head while he was sleeping in the boat for a perch. The moment of realisation of both participants had to be seen to be believed.

Well, that was the easy 'know your birds' stuff. Now came the difficult bit, to prove that they were breeding on the islands. The first sound evidence of ornithological real estate was a family of Crested Terns. The youngest, not yet fledged, were flopping about in shallow water and were easy to catch and photograph. They couldn't have flown to Île Lubine so they must have been born there. More evidence began to accrue. Noddy Terns were in evidence, showing their peculiar 'we got a nest' behaviour. Actual nests of both the Indian Mynah and the Madagascan Fody were empty but with firm signs of recent habitation. Perhaps the most exciting find, at least expedition-wise, was when our chosen insignia, a delicate Fairy Tern, nested about 40 feet above the basha which housed our four generators. There above the noise and well within the plume of exhaust fumes she laid and then incubated the egg, turning it with great care on the flat parts of a branch of a hibiscus tree which served as a nest.

This story has an unfortunate end, but one that must be told. The whole team were fired with a great enthusiasm to get our bird and her egg on film. So the contingent from the Royal Engineers swung into action and built the most extraordinary tripod out of tree trunks with a platform for the camera, at egg level. This edifice was prepared as a surprise while Mont was away on a trip. The blow came when felling the last piece of wood needed for the top platform. The branch selected by the party on the forest floor was actually the one on which the tern was nesting, so down came the Hibiscus, Tern, egg and all and down came the wrath of the expedition on Don. He was not allowed to forget it and a chuggle was hung on the tripod as a reminder. When Christmas came each member of the expedition was given a special task, to make a gift for one of the other members. The opening of the gifts and the reading of the long instructions which went with most of them took up about two very hilarious hours after dinner. The biggest laugh was for the present from George Russell for Don Phillips. A Mark II Tern's egg made of polypropylene and shaped, well, trapezoid. The inscription with the egg read: 'Tern's Egg – guaranteed Royal Engineer Proof, Mark II.' Although Chuggles lost his conservation badge the Terns soon forgot and forgave because just before we left the island the same pair were back in position having another go.

Certainly the most spectacular residents were the Myna and the Fody, the former for its raucous cry as it clattered away through the coconut fronds, the latter for the bright scarlet of the male, while in mating trim. The female Fody is a rather inconspicuous brown bird not unlike the European House Sparrow. Fodys are in fact the House Sparrows of the tropics, filling the same niche, always close to man and his habitation.

Whether man actually took the Fody to Egmont with him or whether it just followed along down the chain of atolls, we shall probably never know. However it got there, there is no doubt that it is still there fifty years after the last permanent human residents left. Each island is in fact a network of territories, the bounds of which are jealously guarded by the resident Fody. Each family has its own fully detached woven house suspended from a convenient spot in the tree canopy, in the middle of about 12 hectares of land, which puts the total atoll population at about thirty-five pairs. The factor which limits the size of the Fody population is the abundance of seeds which form the bulk of the birds' diet. The key to their survival is population control determined by their territorial behaviour and their hanging nest, and thereby hangs more than one tale.

During man's short sojourn on the islands he did a number of catastrophic things. First he removed much of the natural vegetation and planted coconuts, at a rough guess a million of them. Most of them, or at least of their direct descendants, are still there in serried ranks which arise from great piles of rotting coconuts and leaves. I well remember saying to my family to quell their fears relating to Daddy's safety, that I was safer on the expedition than I would be walking around London. This was untrue, motor cars come at you on ground level, coconuts come straight down obeying the laws of gravity, and a coconut from 90

The 'nest' (although I use the word guardedly) of a Fairy Tern.

To prove it the Fairy Tern (our expedition's emblem) on the nest.

feet can produce grave effects.

Secondly, man introduced animals, some, like pigs, goats and chickens, were of direct use and were therefore introduced on purpose, others like the cat and dog as pets and still others, like the rat, by accident, to become as they still are the scourge of the Egmont Isles. In the end economics, and perhaps in part the rats, beat man and in 1936 he gave up trying to get a living before they did, and pulled out leaving the silent isles of coconut as a fitting epitaph to man's failure. The fascinating thing is that although in 1937 the islands were infested with goats, pigs and chickens, by 1972 the only feral animal left was the rat supreme in his island home and living, one presumes, on an exclusive diet of coconuts, supplemented with the occasional egg stolen from some nest and presumably anything else which came their way. Rats were everywhere and they soon learned to eat everything we had brought with us. Polythene appeared to become part of their diet along with processed cheese, dry batteries, even human hair if it happened to stick out through the mesh of a mosquito net at night.

So the main problem which faces all the resident birds is how to raise a family in safety from the rats. The choice of method is somewhat restricted, being either to suspend your nest from, or to lay your egg on a thin branch so that the route to the nest may be guarded. On the

An abandoned chicken still finds food on the islands.

One of the bronze propellors, all shiny.

The El Maren 1920, fish farm by accident, shelter just where it is most needed on the most exposed point of the reef.

other hand ground nesting species like the Crested Tern must just take pot luck, and ninety-nine times out of a hundred they must lose out, at least on Egmont Isle.

Île Sudest abounded with rats. All of them were the same sort of ubiquitous black rat with its long tail and predominantly grey/black coloration. This animal is so common on a world scale that even the scientific fraternity couldn't think of a special name for them and just used the Latin *Rattus rattus*. Careful search in the daytime showed that there were fewer rats either on Lubine or Sipaille than on Sudest and, talking of names, Sipaille is the local name for the Coconut Crab and both the latter islands abound with this science-fiction-type animal.

The Coconut Crab, or to give it its proper name, Robber Crab, can grow to around 3 feet in length and, as one of the names suggests, they eat coconuts, from which they simply tear the fibrous husk with relative ease. No one, as far as I know, has ever tried the acid test of shaking hands with the large pincers, but since a juvenile one made a

The dreaded coconut or robber crab.

large hole in Ted Hinton-Clifton's foot through a pair of coral boots and a thick sock we treated them all with the respect they deserved. Nevertheless we kept our eyes open for a record crab and eventually found the grandmother of them all living in a hole full of coconut fibre in a hollow tree. She was a beauty and was more than able to look after herself and her brood of about 200 eggs cradled beneath her broad tail. Her pincers, though made of material biochemically akin to our hair, a cocktail of protein and calcium, were quite capable of scoring the metal blade of a machette. When one day we found her completely dismembered, all the meat gone, it was difficult not to glance furtively over one's shoulder scanning the hollow recesses of the coconut groves for her assailant.

The result of a brief population census was quite conclusive. Île Sudest has few Robber Crabs, but lots of rats, whereas the balance is reversed on Lubine and Sipaille. The dearth of Robber Crabs on Sudest could readily be explained by the fact when the islands were actively farmed for copra the population lived on Sudest and it is likely that here they actively destroyed the crab which menaced their livelihood and also makes very good eating. Could it be that in the absence of the crabs the rats have flourished?

Proof of such a supposition would take many months of detailed investigation; however one simple experiment did seem appropriate, and that was to see how the two animals reacted towards each other. A large crab was therefore penned and provided with a plentiful supply of succulent coconuts. The arena was thus prepared. Come evening time there was no need to go and hunt for the rats; they were swarming inside the pen sharing the coconuts with the crab without any sign of fear. Another experiment bit the dust and our crab, codenamed Freda, retired up the coconut palm which happened to support among other things a pair of Noddy Terns and a Fody's nest, and the birds didn't like it at all.

It would appear then that the Coconut Crab is not the Pied Piper of Egmont but it would also appear that both could represent a potential hazard to all resident birds wishing to set up house. So Mont's Motel, although a delightful setting with all 'mod cons', has some major drawbacks when it comes to the ornithological survival stakes.

Mature *Takamaka* on Ile Lubine (Egmont), no wonder the locals used to use them to make boats.

The flower of *Scaevola taccada* first live sea defences of Egmont.

The flowers of the *Calophyllum inophyllum* the *Takamaka*.

A 'Rose' by any other name could smell no sweeter *Barringtonia asiatica*.

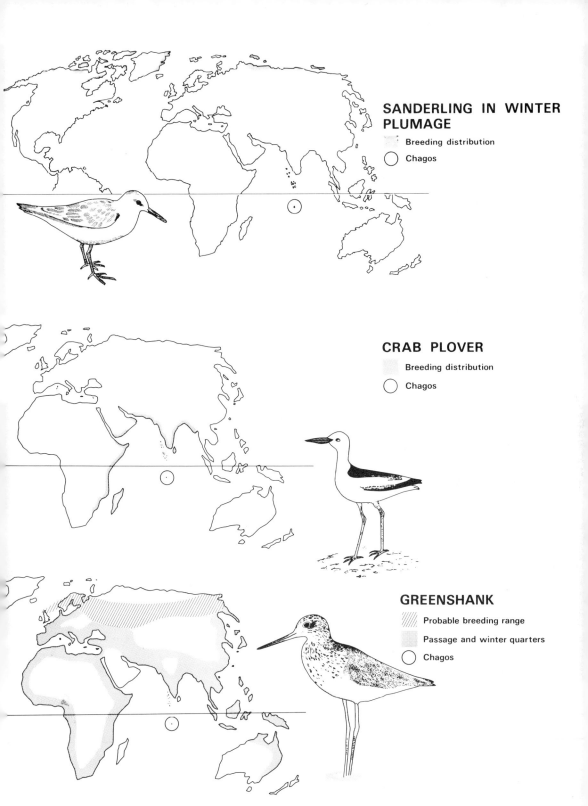

SANDERLING IN WINTER PLUMAGE

- Breeding distribution
- Chagos

CRAB PLOVER

- Breeding distribution
- Chagos

GREENSHANK

- Probable breeding range
- Passage and winter quarters
- Chagos

A long way to fly each year.

As the weeks went by the number of different types of birds recorded on the atoll continued to climb and by 8th December, the half-way stage of the expedition, the total number reached thirty-eight, thus exceeding the total number recorded in the past for the whole Chagos Archipelago. The final grand total of fifty far exceeded our wildest hopes and must make Egmont of prime importance in relation to the Indian Ocean bird movement as a whole.

The vast quantity of birds moving in the vicinity of Egmont was apparent every evening when the air space just above the breaking waves and for about a mile outside the reef ridge was jammed with birds heading north. Closer inspection showed that the majority of these were Boobies of one sort and another and, as is typical when Boobies are in the vicinity, Frigate birds were there at angels one-five, waiting their chance. Both these birds are colonial nesters and the one colony preys upon the other. The Boobies range out from their nesting sites for over 20 miles, feeding on the productive territorial waters of the atoll. The Frigates get their nourishment second hand, as it were; they soar high up above biding their time and then dive bomb the poor Boobies, keeping on until they give up their meal, which is either caught in mid-air or scooped up from the sea by the Frigates. The aerial drama was re-enacted many times over the shallow waters around Egmont and although the aerobatics of the winners were always marvellously perfect, one could not help feeling sorry for the poor old Booby bird who always appeared to lose out.

There was little doubt that both the antagonists must be nesting on some nearby island and air photographs indicated this to be Danger Island, which lies some 20 miles N.N.W. off Egmont. The question then was why, as they took all the trouble to fly that 20 miles in both directions every day to feed on and around Egmont, have they not colonised the islands of the Egmont group? In the absence of any more positive evidence, a sound hypothesis would appear to be, because of the rats. Both the birds in question are large and therefore cannot make their nest on the highest, thinnest branches. So they would be very prone to rat attack. Also their pattern of colonial life includes a communal mating ritual, and for this reason it is impossible for a single pair to nip in, build a nest and bring up a family. No colony means no

Little Swift 6"

Swallow 7½"

Common Tern
(Winter) 14"

Roseate Tern (Winter) 15"

Little Tern 9"

White tailed
Tropic Bird 16"

Ringed Plover 7½"

Dunlin 7"

Kentish Plover 6¼"

Grey Plover 11"

Turnstone 9"

Wandering Tattler 10" (Winter)

Pintail female 28"

Garganey female 15"

Whimbrel 16"

Bar-tailed Godwit 15"

Curlew 22"

Visitors to Mont's Motel.

mating dance, which means no young and it is much more difficult for a whole crowd to get a full colony of happy families without the rats getting to know.

The saga of Mont's Motel is as long as the list of birds and each really deserves its own fascinating chapter. Two more bird stories must suffice; the first is of George, a Lesser Black-backed Gull. One day George arrived on the scene a somewhat bedraggled juvenile which must have been blown a long, long way from home. He evidently recognised the human being as something he had seen before and he adopted us and our diving boats. Every day George would fly to meet us and gladly accept our compo processed cheese, which we were glad to donate. Day by day his back got blacker and his tail feathers became more like a tail and less like a ragged coronet and day by day he became bolder, balancing on the boat and eventually accepting cheese from the hand. The local birds didn't like him at all and mobbed him whenever he got too close. George took little notice of them and consoled himself for his isolation with human company and processed cheese. When floating on the sea he kept a wary eye out below and would gently lift off if a large fish came into his vicinity. The only day that we forgot to feed George was the day that an unexpected ship called by and that night George checked out to follow the more varied diet which flowed from its scuppers. That night the island was a lonelier place, but at least the list of visitors had been increased by one.

My second and last bird story is about another one which was a bit of an embarrassment. During the last evening of the expedition we were taking final stock and one of our most important stock lists was that of the birds we had seen. It came to forty-nine species in all. I remember saying to Mont, 'It's good it wasn't exactly fifty as no one would have believed us.' No sooner had I said it than Ray Perren walked in and said, 'Filthy scientificos, don't leave your birds about!' He deposited a perfect carcass on the pile of boxes that was our make-shift table. It was a Common Tern – number fifty on the books!

Commander Alan Baldwin, O.B.E., M.I.Mech.E., R.N.: Leader.
Commander Steve Lowick, M.I.Mech.E., M.R.A.S., R.N.: Deputy Leader.
Lieutenant Tom Peake, R.N.: Stores Officer.
C.P.O. Keith Whitehouse: Engineer.
C.P.O. 'Sharkey' Ward: Radio Engineer.
Sergeant 'Boots' Allistone, R.M.: Boats Officer.
Major Adrian Lane, Military Police: Camp Commandant.
Captain Gordon Raku, R.S.: Communications Officer.
Sergeant Dave Young: Surveyor.
Corporal 'Arry' Carden: Chef.
Squadron Leader Dave Rickard, R.A.F.: Assistant Diving Officer.
Flt Lieutenant Clive Studd, M.B., Ch.B, R.A.F.: Doctor.
Chief Technician 'Stan' Stanley: Electrical Engineer.
Sergeant Ray Pringle Scott, A.B. Soup.: Photographer.
David Bellamy, Ph.D., B.Sc., F.L.S.: Chief Scientist.
Mont Hirons, M.Sc., F.R.M.S., M.I.Biol., M.B.O.U.: Ornithologist.
Charles Sheppard, B.Sc.: Zoologist.
Mike Ballentyne, M.I.C.E., M.I.Struct.E., M.I.E. Austr.

BBC

Peter Crawford, B.Sc.: Producer.
Maurice Fisher: Cameraman.
'Dicky' Bird: Sound.

The Crew of the Four Friends

Warren Blake: Master.
Tue Blake: Master's Wife.
Keith Morris: 1st Mate.
Chang: Engineer.
Annie: Crew.
Robin: Crew.
Mark: Crew.

The Other Half of Paradise

10.
"Baggy Wrinkles"
and the Four Friends

It was 21.30 hours 18th January 1975. The R.F.A. *Resurgent* was lying about 1½ miles off Eagle Island. Contact had been made with the advance party who had been on the island for some ten days and our plans for a rendezvous at first light had been laid. The great grey ship turned away from the reef ridge back to the safety of deeper water. I had turned in to grab a few hours of sleep before our 05.00 call and despite the excitement of the situation, sleep came at once as I was lulled by the motion of the friendly ship.

Rat-a-tat-tat! The cabin door opened; outside stood two junior stewards clutching a paper bag. 'Sorry, sir, I thought the ornithologist was in here, we've got a bird, found it stunned on the deck.' I got up and went with them to rouse Mont from the next cabin. Inside the bag was a medium-sized bird, a Noddy tern to welcome us back to the Chagos? As Mont's hand gently removed the bird from its paper prison both of us gave a gasp of surprise. Its feathers were a smoky black not unlike the tropical night outside. This was no Noddy; its hooked bill and raised nostrils set well back spelt Petrel. Black legs, black feet, black bill, in fact black everything, well, black with a hint of brown, no distinguishing marks except for a slight deep brown window on the upper wing. Sleep was forgotten, out came rulers and notebook; wing 20 mm, bill 22 mm, tarsus 110 mm, left us in no doubt; it was a Bulwer's Petrel, a new record for the Central Indian Ocean and a good omen for everything that was to come.

We had only just got on board the R.F.A. *Stromness*, on our way home from Egmont when I started thinking about the possibility of a return trip. I had stood with Mont and Alan Baldwin taking our last look at that wave-washed gauntlet of life that had occupied all our energies for seventy-three days as it slipped rapidly away from the stern. Down between decks there was ice cold Oranjeboom and my first had hardly hit my stomach when we began planning.

Rats or no rats, Egmont had whetted our appetites, and the data we collected had raised many more questions that it had solved. Is Egmont actually part of the Great Chagos Bank, and if so are its living reefs typical of those of the Bank itself? No less a person than Charles Darwin had pronounced the reefs of the Bank to be dead. Mind you he only did it on the basis of secondhand knowledge gained by Captain Moresby with the help of a lead weight smeared with tallow. Darwin had also concluded from the same survey data that the Chagos Bank was the remnants of a gigantic atoll which is gradually eroding away and slipping out of sight.

Our work on Egmont had shown us that at least one of the atolls of the Central Indian Ocean grows most luxuriantly on its most sheltered flanks. Could it be that the same had been true for Darwin's dead atoll? Around the whole 250 miles of its gigantic perimeter only along the north-western and especially the south-west flank was there any dry land, by name, Nelson, Eagle, Sea Cow, the Three Brothers and Danger Island. In all some eight square miles of tenuously dry land were circumstantial evidence, if not proof, that along this sector of the bank at least the processes of erosion were not going as quickly. The facts fit; every school person knows that the Trade Winds blow from the north-east for part of the year and the south-east for the rest. The scatter of tiny islands are on the most sheltered side of the Bank. The only trouble is that we don't know whether a completely submerged reef can provide protection for something which is more than 50 miles away down wind.

The second main question related to the home of all those sea birds, the third to the coffer dam across the reef channel, the fourth to the source of the hydrogen sulphide, etc. Thirsts temporarily slaked, we rushed up the companionway to strain our binoculars over the rail towards the hazy outline of Danger Island now rushing past on the starboard quarter. I turned to Dickie, Alan and Mont. We shook hands; 'we've done it', and back came the response 'and we'll do it again'.

The *Four Friends*, a 76-foot ketch part-owned and skippered by a New Zealander, Warren Blake, brought the advance party from Gan in the Maldives to Eagle Island via Peros Banhos. She is a thing of great beauty. Her white ferro-concrete hull reflected the blue-green moods of the sea as her sails canvassed strength from the winds which blew from the four quarters of her ocean.

Apart from transporting both the advance and retard party and our fuel supply from Gan, the main task of the ketch was to provide safe transport between the islands and the transects to be surveyed.

Her crew, not forgetting the dog, which boasted a Cambodian passport, added a truly international flavour to our terribly English expedition. It also injected a certain amount of couth into what otherwise was an all male outing. The rules of the base camp were thus set right from the start, 'Six days thou mayest labour in the nude but on the seventh dress more decorously as the campsite may be invaded by those of the opposite sex!'

The adventures of the trendsetters had begun way back in late November when the *Four Friends* plus seven left Singapore on the first leg of the journey to Gan. Her log read like a millionaire's cruise, *Singapore, Penang, Grand Nicobar, Maldives*, a route that almost follows the lines of coral distribution which radiate out from their region of highest diversity in Indonesia.

A major engine malfunction did not unduly hamper the journey as fresh winds brought the ketch to port in good time. Instant signals brought spares winging R.A.F.-wise from Singapore and the necessary repairs were completed in double quick time. A gentle and well-oiled purr from below decks signalled success. Up came the anchors, and the expedition proper was under way.

The ketch hurried away from the pendant on the necklace of the Maldives, south towards the little-known waters of the Great Chagos Bank. The first landfall in the vastness of the Indian Ocean is Peros Banhos, placid outlier of a world of hidden reefs and uncharted shoals.

96

Thanks to the ferroconcrete perfection of the *Four Friends* and her crew we were able to survey Darwin's dead atoll.

Commercial man has been to Peros Banhos and lost his struggle for survival, only a ghost town, coconut palms and rats mark his failure.

Peros Banhos was, for more than 100 years, the focal point of the culture of the Bank, a culture founded on the white of copra and enriched by people of many races, Africans, Indians, Mauritians, Seychellois and Chinese, a short sad story of human endeavour finally defeated by the quasi-economics of the outside world. Founded in 1836 it survived for almost 150 years, coming to an abrupt end in 1973 when its people were returned whence their predecessors had come and the once productive coconut groves were left to the silence of twentieth-century neglect.

The ghost settlement stands, as yet intact, the altar in the simple church daubed with plastic flowers; ordered rows of beds stand waiting in the hospital; a brace of swings reciprocate in the loneliness of the wind as a donkey foal brays its first few days away. Limes, breadfruit, lush lemons and plantains intersperse their plenty between the decaying houses, many of which bear on their inner walls sad graffiti telling us that warm, vibrant life was here and that many wanted to stay.

The transient culture is gone, a culture which brought new order to the patchwork of natural vegetation, a patchwork of natural forest evolved through time, now replaced by great palms which throw their leaves upwards in a vain attempt to shut off the tropic sun.

In that 150 years the main islands of the Chagos Archipelago, Peros Banhos, Salomon, Diego Garcia, Egmont and Eagle, were all tamed by man, a fact that is recorded in the scant histories of the region. But what of Nelson, Danger, the Three Brothers and Sea Cow, each too small and/or too distant for more than semi-permanent settlement? These were to be the object of the land survey on our second expedition. What would we find?

After two days in the lagoon of Peros, the *Four Friends* left her last safe anchorage and headed south by west for Eagle.

Eagle island was, as expected, an elongate exclamation mark of dry land fringed with burning white sand and a cruel halo of reef with what, from the sea, looked like a solid infill of palms. Sea Cow, an almost circular island, formed the dot subtending the mark but her reefs looked as impenetrable as the coconut groves of Eagle and her size was too small to provide a lee shore on which to lay a new home anchorage.

The north end of Eagle was more hopeful. There the reef front

It said the boats were inflatable and the sharp coral rock proved it again and again.

bowed out to produce a sheltered lagoon with what appeared from the air photographs to be a channel connecting the open sea to the calm of protected water within. Just north of the lagoon shallow water provided an anchorage, protected from the south by the curve of the reef front and from the east by the bulk of the island.

The inflatables were loosed and with care were nosed into the turbulence of cross waves that hid the mouth of the lagoon channel. Once committed, the only safe course of action was to ride the back of the biggest wave in towards the island. There was deep water, but over to port, and the pull of the wave was too great to steer for the clear passage in time. To lose nerve now would mean catastrophe, for only the height of the breaking wave gave enough freeboard to clear the reef front.

The bow of the inflatable dropped, jack-knifing her buoyancy tubes. There came no crunch, no grating. The advance party were inside the lagoon, knowing that their first task was to buoy the channel to ensure no further mistakes.

Frantic work then began, unloading the multitude of stores, clearing the brush and the accumulations of coconut from the chosen camp site, leaving enough room to house the tents and to keep the rats at bay. Oh, yes! man had left his rats behind on Eagle Island.

That night for the first time since leaving Gan, the members of the advance party ate a cooked meal. The large load of petrol carried as deck cargo on the ketch had made cooking *en route* an impracticable task. This was however no hardship because one of the great fascinations of Vietnamese cooking is what can be done with fish in the raw, and Tue Blake was honorary chef to the advance party. On the evening of the 19th January the members of the expedition experienced their first landlocked night on the Chagos Bank and now the further delights of Vietnamese cuisine – hot this time.

To conclude this chapterette, just for the benefit of anyone who didn't know, 'baggy wrinkles' are sail protectors, to be more exact those things that look like gigantic woolly caterpillars threaded on to the main stays which hold up the masts of any well maintained ketch. They are constructed of rope ends and their construction is very wearing on the fingers, good punishment for any miscreant member of the crew.

The 19th January was a day of hard, hard work, perhaps best forgotten but maybe not; we were after all back in paradise and that made everything seem less like work. So did the fact that a large section of the complement of the R.F.A. *Resurgent* turned to it and carried a large part of the various burdens. Without them the job of unloading would have taken a week. Thanks to them it was accomplished in two days. The heaviest and bulkiest items of equipment and stores were of course the most important, galley, air bank, diesel fuel for the ketch and a recompression chamber in case of problems when diving.

Protected, located, watered (with special catchments filling inflatable reservoirs), and victualled, we watched *Resurgent* disappear over the horizon. The fantastic routine of diving was to begin in the morning. Thirty-six transects were to be surveyed. Mont and I walked off into the coconut grove to begin the land operations; it was silent for want of birds but alive with the scuttling of rats, and rich with the promise of discoveries to be made.

11.
The Character of the Three Brothers

Of all the islands we planned to visit, the Three Brothers held the greatest promise. Never visited by a scientist let alone a diver, these scraps of land could hold the clue to some or all of the thousands of birds that had flown past Egmont Island twice each day.

We had not long to wait, for hardly had the expedition gained breath from the unloading than the research programme was in full swing, the first long trip being a visit to the Three Brothers. '05.00 hrs. *Reveille*, a hasty compo breakfast, on board the ketch by 06.00' so the orders of the day read, and that, to even Steve Lowick's surprise, actually happened. The *Four Friends* plus twenty-four ploughed her way on engine alone north through a medium sea, which left all not so good sailors a little queasy, even though the whole journey lasted no more than ninety minutes. The pangs of *mal de mer* were however soon forgotten in the lee of Middle Brother where gear for a three-day stay and at least twenty-four dives had to be off-loaded. It was during the off-loading that the full promise and excitement of these, the smallest islands, became clear.

The air above Middle Brother was alive with birds; the numbers – even admitting the inaccuracies of long distance guesstimations – were unbelievable. Black spirals of Frigates thermalled upwards watching for the ordered flights of Boobies returning, crops gorged, from their feeding ground. Lower, the air space seemed to be choc-a-bloc with Terns. Everywhere we looked there were birds.

Equally large clouds of birds seemed to be massed above each island, although even through binoculars it was impossible to make out what species they were. We didn't know at the time that each Brother had its own character, a character in part dependent upon the extent of man's past intervention in the natural order but made manifest by the type of birds which had taken up residence, presumably since his evacuation. The vegetational canopy of each island was alive with residents of various sorts, rather like the famous hat of Edward Lear's Quangle Wangle.

Middle Brother had little to hide; even from the air photographs it showed an open character. Its 7·8 hectares of dry land were flanked on one side by the raging torrent of open sea, protected only by a narrow reef flat and a fully exposed reef ridge. On the other side the island was lapped by calm blue water, a miniature lagoon complete with coral heads and protected by a circlet of reef that bows out into the open ocean. Middle Brother is in fact an atoll in the making, not unlike an Egmont in embryo.

One narrow channel punches through the reef, its branches leading the inflatables to the safety of calm water and an easy landing on a steeply shelving beach of coral sand.

Stores for three days were quickly unloaded, survey tents erected, tea brewed up and the dive parties were off, leaving some landsters to start their own voyage of exploration.

The periphery of the island was covered with the typical low scrub of *Scaevola* and *Tournefortia*. From the gnarled branches of the latter curious bills surmounted by sharp eyes pointed at the new invaders. Some of the birds were no more than a ball of white fluff, agitated bundles of down; others, still at the awkward growing up age, suddenly realised the absence of mum as we approached. However, the majority of the nests were occupied by an adult Red Foot Booby in all its pristine glory faithfully guarding two eggs or one fledgling. Many of the birds were fast asleep, bills hidden in regulation fashion beneath their sleek primary feathers. So they stayed until you actually brushed their perch, when, waking to the full indignity of their swaying position, they would begin the beak-jabbing routine, back and forward, back and forward, heads moving in an anticlockwise direction, to warn you away with a 'come any nearer if you dare'. If you did, perhaps true to their names, they would lose heart and back off to make one of those typical gannet-type take-offs, all flap and little lift.

The booberies were in fact full to overflowing and it was not an impossible task to make a complete population census, which came out at 450 pairs. The figure does not include the many young snickering their beaks into the heat and waiting not too patiently for the next fish meal which would provide them with all their requirements both for food and water.

Above the booberies, the coconut palms soared up into the heat, their compound leaves drooping for want of water. Apart from their central sprout of flowers and developing nuts, many of them were daubed with the black shapes of the Frigates. Black feathers and a tropical sun are not the happiest of combinations, a fact belied by the way in which each Frigate holds its wings, part open to act as a heat exchanger across every cooling breeze. The Frigates took little or no notice of us humans and if they did decide to move themselves their take-off was effortless compared to that of the Boobies. Up they would go with a gentle flap to join in the effortless flight of the others soaring above on the island's own special spiral of heat.

Engrossed in the routine of survey we found our first day had soon gone, and the smell of guano distilled with the fragrance of the *Scaevola* flowers told us that evening was coming. Twilight in the tropics is so ephemeral that it has passed almost before you have had time to savour it. The temperature begins to drop and with it goes the light. Our first night among the Three Brothers was about to begin. With the gathering darkness the air became heavy with sound, the sound of tens of thousands of terns calling to each other. The noise was all-enveloping, so much so that it was impossible to locate the exact source of the cacophony. The beams of powerful torches swept the undergrowth and stabbed up into the palm leaves, but they revealed nothing except Boobies and Frigates blinking in the new experience. The beams stabbed higher into the velvet air but their power was insufficient to locate the cloud of birds. It was not until some wisps of cumulus spread across the background glare of the stars that they were picked out, black dots against the wisps of white. Thousands upon thousands of Sooty Terns for some unknown reason were clamouring their night away. During the day, the beaches had held more than their fair share of these dapper black and white terns. More were out to sea, flitting over the waves, their bright white eye flashes gleaming from sooty cap making them easily recognisable even at a distance. Sooty Terns were definitely in residence on the island, but not in this number. From where had they all come and why?

By this time everyone in the camp was beginning to worry, not about the origin of the birds but whether they would get any sleep that night. However the clamour stopped almost as abruptly as it started, leaving enough silence for everyone. Thank goodness because tomorrow was another working day, and with it more surprises were to come.

It soon became clear that most of Middle Brother had been affected by man. Apart from its *Scaevola* fringe little of the vegetation could be called natural. Open glades between clusters of coconut palms were covered by a turf of sedge punctuated by rows of deep holes each dug in the rock to house the base of a palm, most of which had long since gone if indeed they had ever managed to grow. Strutting about in the midst of all this man-made vegetation almost as if to prove the point was a small flock of *Gallus gallus*, the common or back garden hen. One

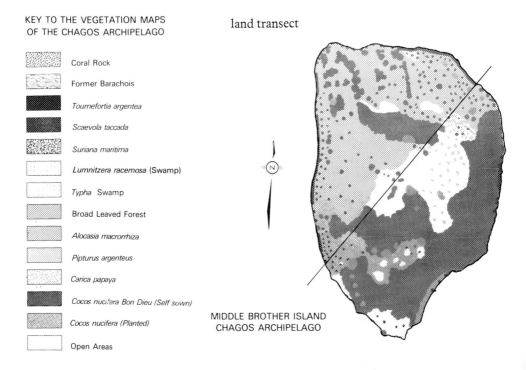

KEY TO THE VEGETATION MAPS
OF THE CHAGOS ARCHIPELAGO

land transect

Coral Rock

Former Barachois

Tournefortia argentea

Scaevola taccada

Suriana maritima

Lumnitzera racemosa (Swamp)

Typha Swamp

Broad Leaved Forest

Alocasia macrorrhiza

Pipturus argenteus

Carica papaya

Cocos nucifera Bon Dieu (Self sown)

Cocos nucifera (Planted)

Open Areas

MIDDLE BROTHER ISLAND
CHAGOS ARCHIPELAGO

can only presume that their ancestors were left to rule the roost by the last of the coconutsters who must have left this tiny island to its own devices well over fifty BOAR (before our arrival). Whether chickens are by nature fainthearted or whether dreadful tales of us human beings had been passed down their chain of ancestry, I don't know, but of all the birds we found on the expedition these were the most timid, taking off as soon as we got anywhere near them. Taking off was in fact the operative word; they could fly, and although they couldn't keep it up for long, if the need arose, they could struggle up to join the Frigates in the trees.

If we needed absolute proof of the absence of rats on the island there it was or rather they were, clucking around well out of sight, with plenty of cheep cheeps to prove the viability of their population. Nice as it was to have the homely sound of eggs on the hoof around the camp-site we didn't really need any further proof of the absence of rats because everywhere we looked there were the speckled eggs of the Fairy Tern, laid wherever the fancy took them from niches on leaning palm trunks to fallen palm leaves on the ground. The stamp of man was well and truly on the face of Middle Brother; the curse of man's rats was not.

The short journey to Big (South) Brother was made exciting on two counts, first by the question of what might be there, nesting for us and secondly because it was going to be a very hairy landing. As there was no convenient lagoon, a direct line across the reef flat was the only method of approach to the second of the Three Brothers. We're riding along on the crest of the wave and as soon as we hit shallow water, it's all out, and the boat must be turned prow out before the next wave brings catastrophe, broadside on. The secret of success lies in the rapidity of the turn. On the first run we all got very wet but we did it and there waiting on the beach was the answer to our other tern problem, the source of the Sooty Terns!

Serried ranks of young Terns, each resplendent in their brown speckled feathers, were jostling to see the fun of us capsizing.

Sooty Terns are gregarious birds, especially during the breeding season, which starts off in a mass display, a ritual fly-about during which the birds pair off ready for the mating. Once paired and mated

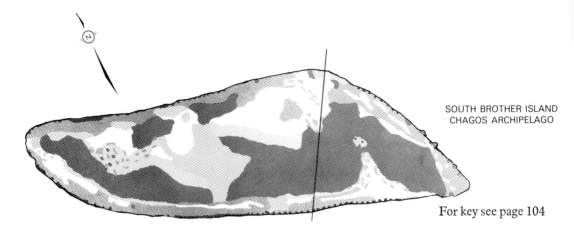

For key see page 104

SOUTH BROTHER ISLAND
CHAGOS ARCHIPELAGO

they lay the eggs in communal laying patches, egg crèches, often in among low vegetation. It was easy to recognise these from afar as, probably due to repetitive use over many generations, they showed up as bald patches among the green of the sedges.

Many of the crèches were silent, littered with the carcasses of the least fortunate of each communal brood, the ones that had not made it in the first struggle to fledge. The fittest had already left to crowd the beaches of freedom, testing their wings against the onshore breeze. Some of the crèches were however still occupied by the young, most of which, though ready to fly, had not yet plucked up their wings of courage. Every now and then a devoted dapper adult would come in to land. Picking out its own young among the clamour of beaks, it would administer the next meal and a 'word' of encouragement.

Here was the ideal opportunity to get down to some real ornithological detective work. It didn't take long to capture and band a hundred of the fledglings from a range of the crèches. Out of all the birds we caught only one was in a bad state, infested with nematode worms to such an extent that we put it quickly to sleep. Perhaps this was one of the reasons for all the infant mortality. The rapid communication of disease is just one of the problems of communal living. The most common affliction of the birds was however some large and rather nasty-looking ticks and no less than thirty-four of our sample had these obnoxious creatures well dug in. We soon learned that the ticks were not very fussy in their choice of hosts and each night we had to perform a ritual of inspection and removal of all ticks that had taken up residence on us.

As each bird was banded it was returned to the crêche ready for its next meal, perhaps their last before their first triumphant take-off. To where would they fly? Were the Sooty Terns of Middle Brother stay-at-homes, or did they regularly commute to other parts of the world? If we were lucky, the bands might provide us with some information.

Almost half of the island was covered with low vegetation eminently suitable for the terneries and a conservative estimate put the breeding population of the small island at around 40,000 pairs. There was little doubt that South Brother was at least one source of the members of the high-flying chorus of the previous night.

Of all the three Brothers, South, or Big Brother as it soon came to be named, bore most evidence of human occupation although the presence of all these ground-nesting birds and a homely flock of hens told us that here again there were no rats. A well, dug deep and neat down into the coral rock, must have been the centre of a semi-permanent 'village'. Now it is part filled with coral talus and forms a convenient 'pot' for a *Morindia* bush and a home for a gaggle of contented hermit crabs living at least in part on its fallen fruit. Ordered groves of palms swathed their way across the island, isolating some of the crêches from the sea. Sheltered from any sea breezes the heat in these bare spots became intolerable at midday and even the baby terns stopped their bickering and cowered in the meagre patches of shade. In the shadow of the palms the dark cool ground was here and there scarred with holes and in the still silence of the groves a telltale rustling emanated from each one; evidence of life below. They were often not burrows in the strict sense but openings into natural holes beneath the palm roots and between the subsurface rocks. Each one contained a bundle of shearwater down from which two dark eyes shone and a bill with a downcurved end complained at being brought up into the light of day.

There were not many such holes on Big Brother but sufficient to prove that Wedge-tailed Shearwaters are in breeding residence.

Apart from its Shearwaters the central Coconuttery shielded another secret, a quite extensive stand of a mysterious broad-leaved tree we could not identify. Was this a remnant of the forest that originally covered the islands? Man first came to the Chagos to collect wood from 'the Big Trees' which grew there. Had he indeed left some of the smaller less accessible islands alone? Whatever the answer, these particular Big Trees were the proud possession of the local population of Red Foot Boobies, and of course up above on the palm fronds were the Frigates staring out across the sea to Little Brother away to the south and almost lost in its own ring of surf. Big Brother had much more to reveal but time was short on this the first reconnaissance trip and we had more pressing work to do.

Little Brother was going to be a difficult character to get to know. No lagoon tempted us with sheltered water, and the small size of the island made the likelihood of a lee shore unlikely to say the least except on a very calm day.

That day was not very calm, and enormous waves irregularly thumped in on all the beaches, sending spray high into the air. Anchoring the ketch in the calmest area the team proceeded by inflatable to that point at which the rollers start to take over the tiller. Here a 56-pound sinker was dropped over on the end of a long line and the boat let out to ride just outside the line of breaking waves. Dave Rickard, resplendent in jungle green, joined the next wave, a stout rope fixed around his waist, and was rolled ashore. One (the strongest one) down, six to go, but we had the Rickard rope to aid us on our way. Once within the grip of the wave there was nothing you could do but enjoy it, that is until the shallows came painfully close. The reef rock was full of deep, waterscoured holes, its surface covered with the slime of red seaweeds, not at all the place to be caught by the next wave, but of course you were and thus arrived in an undignified heap on the beach. Once you had actually done it, it didn't seem too bad, so back and forth we went unloading the gear, all waterproofed in regulation fashion.

The last member of the team to come on shore was Mont, who up to that moment had been watching the birds, trying to keep his mind off the ordeal to come. Mont cannot swim, and it took even a good swimmer quite a lot of courage to chuck himself into that boiling maelstrom, but over he went into the arms of Dave Rickard and myself and together we clawed our way along the rope.

Mont emerged, bedraggled but beaming and together we all walked up the beach into the arms of paradise. The landing may have provided its own special problems but so it had to all other would-be visitors, and if you can't get yourself on, how could you get the wood from the Big Trees back off? So within the ring of palms there was the natural forest waiting to be discovered. It wasn't completely untouched. Palms and paw paws showed that man had braved the landings many times but today the birds reign supreme.

The forest is structured as if for their particular benefit. Emergent palms sprout frigates to the sky while below the broad-leaved canopy is decked with the untidy nests of Red Foot Boobies jostling for space among the spreading branches. Lower still the younger trees and bushes, though daubed with guano, support neat masses of sticks each marking the home of a Little Reef Heron. In each of the 'matchstick' nests there were two or three just-hatched chicks crying their plaintive 'I want my dinner' in full earshot and eyeshot of the frigates high above.

Around this centre of avian industry the sheltering ring of *Scaevola* and *Tournefortia* bushes provide protection for both the island and the main populations of Red Foots. Crump, crrump – something large is moving through the underbrush; it is a large brown bird that rolls as it walks; crump crrump.

This was our first sighting of a fabulous Brown Booby bird and we followed her out through the scatter of bushes and on to their main nesting ground, an amphitheatre of lush greensward looking from a distance as if it was regularly mowed by some fastidious gardener. The plants which made up the lawn were two herbs with more or less succulent leaves, and the mowing machine in question was the salt laden wind and spray. The greensward ran to the edge of the island which fell away at this point in a series of magnificent cliffs all 15 feet of them, and that is magnificent for a coral atoll. It was a most fantastic place. Everywhere we looked there was a Brown Booby, or at least signs of their nest sites, each one a compressed patch of soft vegetation, often with two eggs, their true soft green-blue colour showing through the outer limy layer. In some the eggs were all a-crack and grey india-rubber-type chicks were beginning to struggle out, while in others little balls of down or white masses of fluff scolded at the intruders. Mums and Dads sat brooding and preening as others skimmed in low over the waves topping the cliff-tops to make their awkward landing run, back home from another fishing trip. The whole life-cycle of the Brown Booby was there for the taking and cameras clicked as proud parents lifted up their ample feathers to let us record the whole thing in detail.

These open green patches appeared to be the best sites for these fascinating but ungainly ground nesters, for they provided more than adequate launch-pads straight out to the feeding-grounds. Not all the birds were lucky enough to have availed themselves of one of the best sites and many had been forced to raise their young further from the sea in among the shade of the forest. Later, detailed study showed that the population was much larger than we had at first anticipated, in fact the Brown Boobies were in residence around the whole margin of the island, a total of 300 pairs.

Once within the margin the big birds were left behind. The going got very precarious as the whole rich deposit of humus beneath the big trees was completely undermined by burrows, so much so that it was impossible to walk very far without breaking through the crust into the galleries below. Progress in among the burrows was therefore a very slow process, entailing balancing from root to root or testing the shear strength of the ground before daring to put one's weight on the Shearwater below. Careful search revealed that the troglodytes of Little Brother came in two shapes; both Wedge-tailed Shearwaters and Audubon's Shearwaters were there in abundance.

It is not at all easy to tell the two apart, at least at chick stage, and as the parents forsake the young throughout daylight hours, only return-ing to feed them at night, we had to do a lot of measuring and watching to set the records exactly right. Unfortunately one question is still to be answered concerning the burrows of the Brothers. On all the islands that were in part given over to Shearwater real estate there were always some burrows, admittedly just a few, that were too small for Shearwaters. Could they be the homes of the most marine of all birds, the Petrels? All we ever got was the circumstantial evidence of the bird in the bag that had welcomed us back to Chagos.

So it became evident that Little Brother was overflowing with bird life, every niche appeared to be full and every safe site and even the majority of marginal seats were fully occupied. The fly-ways were busy both by day and night as the diversity of species exploited the potential of

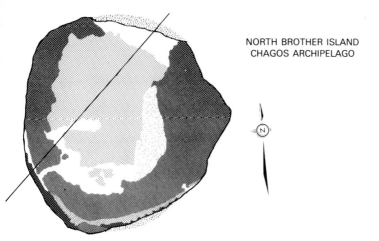

NORTH BROTHER ISLAND
CHAGOS ARCHIPELAGO

For key see page 104

these two hectares to the full. Were the noisy acrobatics of the Sooty Terns just a prelude to pairing or could it have some other meaning? Any land mass, however large, offers only a finite potential for every species; once full then some of the population must move on. Perhaps there is some selection during the aerial display. Is it here, high in the night air that decisions are taken, the strongest gaining the right to the welcome of the Brothers, the rest pushed by some instinct, to fly off in search of fresh 'fields' on which to nest? Does the mid-air council decide which birds shall return to fill and service the crêches and which, like the Lemmings, would have to go, no, not to commit suicide, but perhaps to die in the age-old quest for new land on which to live.

Perhaps our hundred birds, banded in the cause of science, will one day provide some new evidence to help us understand the full implications of that evolutionary dogma Survival of the Fittest.

Before we took our leave of Little Brother there was one more habitat that still remained to be investigated, those rocky cliffs at the edge of the main colony of the Brown Boobies. In among the holes and crannies worn by the spume of the white waves two birds found their own safe sites in which to lay their precious eggs. One was without doubt a Noddy Tern, for the eggs were well guarded by the parents. The other was more difficult, for only the eggs were there, white speckled with dark brown. There was no other clue and so it remained a mystery until much later, as you will see.

III

Interesting as the hardy rocksters were, their chosen home itself held a special fascination. These were no random rocks piled high by the onslaught of massive seas, they were real cliffs constructed of layer upon layer of corals, their skeletons looking much the same as in the days when they grew, reef rock with the corals fossilised *in situ* way above high water mark, an impossible state of affairs. Reef-forming corals cannot grow up above sea level, so since the formation of this stretch of reef either the atoll must have risen up or the sea level gone down.

Whichever of the theories is true, this section of Little Brother is undoubtedly a raised reef. It is interesting to note that the Percy Sladen expedition had in 1916 reported the possibility of raised reefs in the Chagos. We were standing high and dry on the evidence, slap bang in the middle of the Indian Ocean.

The exact reason for the existence of raised reefs is still a bit of a mystery. The most widely accepted theory is related to the fact that at some time in the not-too distant geological past the world's mean sea level has stood at a higher level than it now is. If this is true, why should only one of the Brothers have got the rise? The nearest raised reefs to our elevated friend so far recorded in the literature occur in Aldabra some 2,500 miles to the West and Elephant Island way over to the east. So why did the other two Brothers, Egmont and Eagle, get left out from the rise? The obvious explanation would be that they have sported raised reefs in the past but these have since been eroded away. What we needed was proof.

The story of our first finds on the Three Brothers is almost over but for the fact that they had been evidently joined by a fourth that was not marked on the map, at least not as an island. Moresby's map of 1832 shows a patch of shallow water situated between Big and Middle Brother. Our air photographs confirmed its presence and indicated that it was more than an area of shallows. As we got back on the ketch that night Keith Morris said, 'Today we took a close look at the shoal. That's no shoal, it's another island.'

Pinnacles of reef rock on North Brother mark out both the history of sea levels past and the contemporary presence of a colony of Shearwaters.

The 'Mighty cliffs' of North Brother. Only 15 feet high but proof that the Indian Ocean was at one time 15 foot deeper.

12.

The Big Six

So it was that the expedition began to slip into top gear and points on the map began to become visual images of experience and data to swell the Chagos Banks of knowledge. Surveyors surveyed, botanists botanised, ornithologists ornithologised and of course divers dived. Planning, briefing, de-briefing, this was the order of the dive, an order which ensured that the hours spent under water were a hundred per cent safe and a hundred per cent productive, well, at least ninety-nine point nine per cent. Nothing is ever perfect, except the dive conditions on the Bank. A tremendous amount of supporting work was needed to keep this hive of industrious expeditioning going.

King-pin in the diving end of all this was Big Dave Rickard, the largest, if not the heaviest, member of the Big Six. Apart from the organising of the dive programme each day, there were bottles to be filled, valves to be checked and compressors to be attended. Dave's number two, in task, if not in stature, was Keith Whitehouse, paragon of clean TV, keeper of the non-diving literature and Chief Stoker designate. Together they tended the compressor bank, clucked over second-stage valves and never had a cross word.

Boats were the sole charge of one 'Boots' Allistone. Five inflatables and five engines are quite a handful even for a Royal Marine. However careful a boat handler may endeavour to be, holes will appear in the fabric and sheer pins will fall from engines to the sand beneath and the miscreant is thrice cursed. 'Boots' cursed them that brings and them that takes and when the cursing was all complete he would haul the sagging boat from the oggin, patch the rent, and as he blew in a little pressure he would curse all over again. Major outboard repairs fell to the lot of the Chief Stoker who only really lost his cool when, for the fourth (or was it the fifth?) time in two dives, the starter rope came adrift in the hands of the same unmentionable person.

Twelve hours thou hast tropical light and twelve hours shalt thou labour in the tropical heat. The only unfortunate thing is that twelve hours is not nearly long enough. There are however twelve hours of darkness during which, with the help of the Greenies (electricians), one can labour on in the light of their experience.

Fourth in the Big Six was Stanley Stanley, one time prop forward for the R.A.F., now proprietor of the 'E.E.C.', the Eagle Island Electrical Company. Stan was the master mind of a complex of coughing generators, battery chargers and ring mains designed to keep us all hard at work once the sun had disappeared over the translucent horizon.

Ably backed by Number Five 'Sharky' Ward the Eagle Island Electricity Board was so switched on that it won the Golden Award of the Sand Fly. As soon as the ring mains sprang into glowing life in came the flies by their millions, no billions (English of course) and work had to stop. It is impossible to do anything constructive with your head immersed in a swarm of flies, and even Liar Dice let alone Double Cameroons became impossible to play. Something had to be done.

The interesting thing, at least to insect ecologists, was the fact that they didn't come in every night. Plague proportions were only reached after rain and especially during the periods of high spring tide, when it appeared that the whole population was squeezed up beach to torment us. In the end, the anti sand-fly strategy was simple if not effective. Two Tilley (paraffin) lamps were flashed up and set, hissing in the path of the sand-fly advance. The clouds descended on the lamps and soon a continuous rain of tiny corpses was falling down from the incandescent light to form a truncated pyramid around the base of the lamp. Still they came in, the smell of roasting Sand Fly adding to the distaste of the whole procedure. The flies had won, so it was that the work of the

Ctenella chagosi an important part of the deposit account of the Chagos Bank.

Colonial animals taller than me, Giant Sea Fans.

A ray with a sting in its tail.

camp became punctuated by Sand Fly Evenings spent in the dark in quiet conversation.

On those other evenings when work load and Sand Flies allowed, the range of entertainment soon settled down to one of three, Liar Dice, Master Mind or Escape from Colditz. One of the most vociferous of the Colditz Clan who always played 'Ze Kamp Kommandant' was our own Camp Commandant, 'think tidy' Adrian Lane, Royal Military Police, last but by no means least of the Big Six.

Everything had a place and thanks to the sixteen (no fifteen – Mont was even tidier than Adrian) other untidy members he had a hard time keeping them there. His most magnificent edifice designed to keep us all clean if not tidy was the camp shower system. Water piped from our well and smelling not a little of hydrogen sulphide was lifted by pump into a fifty-gallon drum from which it gushed refreshingly, on demand, that is once you had done your regulation fifty pumps. The idea was to pump before showering as the effort alone made a shower a necessity. After a hard day at the survey there was nothing better than the cooling rush of water and the sound of the next bather pumping his lot up into the tank.

So the Big Six kept us in full working order and every morning the well-oiled hum of satisfied outboards heralded the fact that the dive parties were off to the transect grounds.

Underwater the survey was going to be a much bigger job than that of the Egmont Expedition, with about 300 miles of reef to be at least looked over and a detailed survey of all the reefs around and between the islands to be attempted. Thirty-six transects had been marked on the map and thanks to good weather conditions they were checked off with surprising but never monotonous regularity.

Right from the first dive the range of corals appeared to be as good as that at Egmont with *Ctenella* as an important member of the reef front fauna. Those of us who had been on Egmont missed the friendly shelter of the lagoon, but with the ketch and six near-by islands from which to choose a lee shore, diving was possible on most days. Dive conditions were idyllic, water temperature 24° (75°F) or more, visibility as much as you wanted and always much more than you could take in, and sharks, if not quite as numerous as the best of Egmont, were

usually sufficient to keep the adrenalin up and the shark guard occupied.

The purpose of the underwater survey was threefold. First to ascertain the pattern of reef growth on the submerged 'atoll' rim. Second, to
survey the deep water channels marked on the chart in an attempt to
determine whether they are in reality reef channels in the true sense of
the world. If they were, then we expected to find the black coral
Dendrophyllia and the other members of the normally deep water communities coming up into the light of the shallows. Also there we should
encounter substantial populations of large predatory fish living it up on
the productivity of the tidal currents. Third, we wanted more information about the coral communities and their relations to the life and
growth of the reef front.

It was on one of the routine survey dives on the seaward side of
Eagle Island that one of those underwater pantomimes took place, an
incident which although funny at the time was absolutely hilarious in
afterthought. The chief actors in the scenario were Keith, 'Boots' and
a large Red Snapper, and the scene was set at 100 feet on Transect 39.

At this depth the reef front gradually shelved away to a world of
open sand with restricted patches of coral rock. The chipping of the
collectors hammers brought in the usual school of noisy fish intent on
learning exactly what was going on. Prominent among the pupils were
two medium-sized White Tip Sharks and a large Red Snapper, about
45 pounds, I should think. There in the shelter of a small coral head
was the baddy of the piece, a large black Scorpion fish (hiss boo),
bristling with its own importance as well as its own poisonous fin rays.
Now it just happened that Baddy happened to be sitting on one of the
pieces of coral that was required for the collection. Boots prodded it
away with the business end of the bang stick; enter left, very fast, large
Red Snapper evidently outraged at the treatment of Boss Baddy. Taking elegant evasive action all Boots did was to turn its rage on to the
unfortunate Keith and in it went mouth wide open, raring for battle. It
got it, in the form of a coral hammer around the left gill and it retreated sulking back to the safety of its coral head.

It was also on this transect that another of those sub-aqua memorable moments occurred at a depth of about 45 feet. An open commun-

ity of corals with a number of those enormous table-like Acropores set the stage, in the middle of which an extra large coral head protruded from out of the general flatness. The coral head was alive with fish; I gave up when I had counted what I reckoned were sixty-four different species. One reason I gave up was that Adrian Lane had found a very large Stone Fish. He had thought it was a rock and was about to turn it over when Charles Sheppard pointed out the poisonous spines protruding from its camouflaged back. Nearby, another rock, a real one this time, revealed our most beautiful find to date, a large Sea Slug resplendent with enormous frilly mantle. It was a Spanish Dancer, named so because when she is in free mid-water flight her swimming motions contort the ample mantle into folds like those of a Spanish dancer's dress. She was a big one, over 18 inches long, and as we took her close to the surface the red and yellow concentric hues of this fabulous creature became clearer and so we could film her in full technicolour flight. The film done she was returned to her rock where the Stone Fish still skulked in stony silence.

Accounts of the day's diving always filled the early hours of every evening and in the first few days all the superlatives had been abused again and again. Firm favourites among the transects were those around the Three Brothers where the reef front dropped away from about the 30 feet mark sheer down to and beyond our allowed sphere of dive operation. A 100-foot cliff on land is a mere nothing, a similar cliff under water is a very different matter. It towers up out of the blue blackness of the depth, dwarfing the diver and scattering his bubble plumes which rise current-wise up to the surface. Such a drop off is a place of immense power and interest.

The biggest surprise 'drop off' wise was, however, awaiting discovery right on our Eagle Island doorstep, not 300 yards away from where we dreamed each night about tomorrow's dive. The journey out through the channel was always fraught with the excitement of a rough ride, but once out, the water was moderately calm over a reef front that gently shelved away to 35 feet, then down down it went in a series of gigantic steps down through our 150 feet limit.

It was so easy to do; a short ride, anchors down in 35 feet of water, kit on and there you were, perched on the edge ready to exhale and begin the gradual drift out of the warm multicoloured world of the living reef, down to the blue-black coolness of 150 feet, where the limits of even perfect visibility produce an effect akin to tunnel vision. Your eyes carve out of the depth a tunnel of sharp certainty surrounded by a zone of shark uncertainty, that marks the edge of your halo vision. The bottom of the 'camp' transect as it was called was one of the many places in which the meagre eight minutes allowed on the bottom certainly did start to niggle; it was a place to be savoured not hurried. Perched on the cliff at 150 feet like some vigilant hawk you could look up through a forest of Sea Fans and Whips interspersed with the black candelabras of *Dendrophyllia*, up to the unmistakable outline of the inflatables upon the surface. Questions like 'from how much deeper could you see the boat?' and 'at what depth do the Gorgonians stop?' flood your mind as do the calculations for those decompression stops that would be necessary on a longer dive. An octopus moves across the face of the cliff and the second hand of your watch sweeps away the remnants of dive time. A tap on the shoulder from Steve Lowick, today's dive leader, signals that it is time to go up.

In the annals of naval diving, among the oft-thumbed, well-remembered tables of decompression you can find the facts and figures which pertain to the six-hour rule. They state firmly and simply something like this: 'If you dive to a depth of less than 132 feet (45 m) and the length of your dive rules out the need for a decompression stop, then, six hours after resurfacing you may do another dive to the same depth or shallower without any fear of the bends.' This is the rule and it is a rule that must not be bent on any account. In the knowledge of these facts our diving officers sat down each night armed with a pocket calculator and worked out the pattern of each diving day.

Arise 06.30 to the cries of 'wakey wakey!' and snatches of impossible early morning verse concocted for each occasion by our poet D. O. Steve Lowick. A quick half-pint of tea and on the beach at 07.00 hrs kitted and ready. The early mornings were idyllic, still and cool and although at first we were usually still befuddled with sleep, the boat journey out to the dive station was always exhilarating enough to take the shock out of the moment when you actually hit the water.

The soft dawn light of the above-water world is translated by refrac-

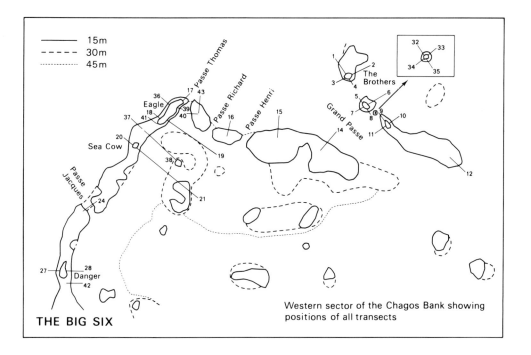

Passe Thomas

32
33
34
35

1
2
The Brothers
3
4

36
Eagle
17 43
18
37 41
39
40
20
Sea Cow
38
19

Passe Richard

16

Passe Henri

15

5
6
Grand Passe
7
8 9
10
14
11
12

Passe Jacques
24

21

27 28
Danger
42

THE BIG SIX

Western sector of the Chagos Bank showing
positions of all transects

tion into a range of sepia tints, the shafts of sunlight reaching like some fantastic aurora down into the blackness at the bottom of the transect line. The early morning fish populations would be about their varied tasks and even the big Groupers looked almost welcoming in the subtle light. A full range of corals were out feeding and it would have been easy to convince yourself that there were many more than later in the day. Careful counting on a number of these dives however showed this to be untrue.

All teams down to depth, all work complete and back in time for a hearty breakfast – and what a breakfast! Early morning diving was good, but early morning fishing was better. Succulent Pompano came rolling in, enough to feed the now ravening horde of divers. Imagine, the freshest of fish, new bread baked the previous night, and on certain occasions steaks of Spiny Lobster tail all washed down with a fresh brew of tea. All this and the knowledge of another dive in the after-noon, this was Scuba heaven.

The home transects were thus ticked off in rapid order, the only problem was that after each dive there was the interminable job of sorting and logging all the specimens. This was the job of the Scientificos, and especially of Charles Sheppard. However, many of the divers who came along to chortle over the wealth of their own sackful would often lend a hand, tying on the labels and wincing at the aroma.

The facts all of a sudden began to fit together, the large map in the mess tent became more and more tatty, each depth ringed and each transect line crossed off as they were completed. Each ringed depth tallied with a reel of black and white film and a box of tagged specimens of all the corals found at that depth, each a permanent record of the *status quo* of the reef community at that point, on that particular day in the history of the reef when *Homo aquaticus* arrived on the scene for the first time.

The photographic record, as on Egmont, was to be the cornerstone of the survey and Ray Pringle Scott and Mike Ballentyne were kept hard at it, tending their cameras between dives, ever-present on the dives clicking and flashing away, and missing the merriment of the early evenings as they sweated it out in the stuffy confines of the dark tent. Every finished negative was acclaimed by the gathered throng and every good shot was claimed as 'that one's mine' by at least six discerning voices.

The photographers came in for a lot of adverse comment, 'Put down that camera and get on with some work!', 'Damn your picture I am not going to put my trousers on!' It was due to the latter that many of the more serious shots of camp activity recorded for posterity had to be censored and filed as restricted, only to be opened by classified personnel.

Apart from his photographic duties, Ray suffered from a childhood fetish. Without giving away vital secrets as to his age, suffice it to say that part of his youth spanned the time when television programmes had intervals and those intervals were filled by fish swimming about in glass tanks. Without these serene and scenic moments of relaxation his days were incomplete. So he had taken up the art of the aquarist and filled his home with cinemascope tanks of living light punctuated with fish. Fortunately for Ray our gear included a monstrous aquarium with a sloping front, B.B.C. Mark I, ideal for filming though, together with all the pumps, filters and other accessories required to make it work. This mass of gadgetry was ideal for keeping our fish man happy and keeping the many specimens we collected alive and ready for filming. The corner of the mess tent was thus adorned with our monster aquarium full of all sorts of monsters of the not so deep. Mealtimes were a joy to behold, with Trigger fish triggering around the rocks, diminutive Groupers changing the colour and intensity of their spots, disgusting elongate sea cucumbers and all manner of crabs rushing about waiting to be fed.

Ray would dash in from a dive clutching a face mask brimming with water and overflowing with the latest prize specimen. Of course everyone wanted to get in on the act and all sorts of things were slipped into the tank when Ray wasn't looking. Worth mentioning are a gaudy blue and red starfish almost 3 feet across, two Portuguese Men of War, diminutive in size, but powerful in sting and an empty compo can, or was it several? The only reason that the latter are worth mentioning is that the larger hermit crabs seemed to accept these in lieu of a new shell. Not worth mentioning were the beer cans, because the crabs couldn't get in, and the Nurse Shark. 'Sharky' Ward caught it and even he knew that it would not fit in even when bent double, but what a prize and a surprise for all the other fish. A new camp rule appeared on the statute books. 'Do not dabble anything in the aquarium before it has spent the requisite period in the quarantine tank and then only under the strict supervision of the Aquarium Officer.'

Despite all these distractions the data rolled in, an average of one hundred coral specimens a day along with Urchins, Sun Stars, Crabs, Shrimps, Sponges. 'You collect it, we'll label it, unless we have one already when it is returned from whence it came.'

The most exciting and air-consuming data, at least collection-wise, were obtained in the areas subject to currents in excess of three knots. Owing to the very tight dive schedule and lack of any precise data relating to tidal movement in the vicinity it was often necessary to dive when the 'current was on'.

Simple precautions minimised the risk, the simplest being to enter the water only while holding on to a rope made fast to the shot line. As soon as you were enveloped in the water you knew all about the hydrodynamics of venturi effects as your mask slipped round to neatly cover your lee-side ear. You soon adjusted to the new life as a model diver in a water-filled wind tunnel and then the hauldown began. More often than not, the deeper you went the less the current. However, once on the bottom, even if the current was too strong to make finning practicable, you could speed along by heaving on all the handholds. If this was impossible, the dive would be aborted, then began the most exhilarating part, sailing back to the top. If you linked your arms around the line and angled your body across current, it was possible to rise to the surface without any effort and what is more exactly at the right speed. All this time the standby divers and dive master up on the surface were on an even redder than usual alert and a long stop was positioned ready in another boat a long way down current. The risks to a diver adrift under such conditions cannot be overstressed and for this reason dives of this nature were only allowed when the sea was dead calm and surface visibility was at a maximum.

Part of each daily dose of excitement came when filling in the day's data on the main base map. It soon became obvious that this whole section of the reef was not dead, it was in fact very much alive. The coral zones as seen on Egmont were well marked and only at the deeper levels did the coral cover fall below about 40 per cent. The strict zonation did break down in places, especially in those where our 'current' diving precautions had to be put into operation and here more often than not the Black deep water *Dendrophyllia* was found up in the shallows. Once this fact was known it was quite easy to pick out these areas simply by donning a mask and peering down over the edge of the boat. There 50 feet or more away the great black colonies were easily visible. Evidently *Dendrophyllia* comes in two growth forms, in still water it forms a three-dimensional bush, while in an area subject to currents it grows as a one-sided colony, its candelabra of branches turned parallel with the current, thus cutting down on water resistance. The shallow water *Dendrophyllia* groves picked out not only the position of the currents but the entrances to the reef channels, exactly where one would expect the main currents to be acting, transects num-

Divers and *Dendrophyllia*, it should be deep but it could be shallow depending on the exact location of the dive.

bers 17 and 3 to date. Here was the proof we were looking for. Darwin's reef, though living, was beginning to reveal all the attributes of an atoll.

The other fact which became increasingly clear as the transect work went on was that on the lagoonward side of the reef the corals were both more abundant and more luxurious than they were on the corresponding seaward side. Sometimes the differences were not very great, but the only real exceptions to the rule were near the entrances to the reef channels where currents took over to play their own particular role.

It is evident that here in the central Indian Ocean the coral communities exist in a state of dynamic equilibrium with the body of living water which constantly ebbs and flows its way through the gigantic submerged atoll. In normal circumstances the more sheltered water provides the best habitat for coral growth and in such places the full zonation exists. Rough water on an exposed shore not only disturbs and breaks up the shallow water communities, but exposes the whole reef front to the problem of scour and reduced light caused by more solid matter suspended in the water.

Water currents add another dimension both to the problems and potential of life on the reef front, aiding the growth of most types of corals at least up to an optimum point. As the currents get stronger they carry not only organic particles in suspension but also sand and other mineral matter which scours the bottom clean of coral growth. At the other end of the scale if the water is too still then deposition of sediment can smother and kill the corals. When Captain Moresby carried out his survey over a hundred years ago his long boats could never have approached the living reef front for fear of capsizing. Likewise within the channels they would have steered clear of the edge, keeping to the well-scoured central channels. No wonder his trailing tallow revealed only a bottom of coral talus, sand and mud for all he was able to sample was the white world below the living reef and within the great bowl of the lagoon, a world devoid of coral growth but full of other forms of life.

13.
"Grotting"
or What the Commander
Really Means

The scene was set for an after-dive court of enquiry. Major Adrian Lane to take the stand, charge to be laid by Commander Baldwin. The charge read as follows, 'Whilst on a routine coral collecting dive your team was seen grotting. All the members of my team witnessed this heinous crime while on the shot line doing a decompression stop.' Major Lane told the court, 'What the Commander really observed was that after completion of our regulation coral dive we turned our efforts and remaining air to the cause of conchology. Furthermore if the Commander looks in the standing orders of the expedition he will find that it is my duty to look after this aspect of the research programme.'

Exhibit No. 1 was placed on the upturned compo box, it was a sack of rough hessian bearing the number 36, a definite article of issue to all transect teams. The sack was gently tipped on to the makeshift table and out poured a stream of beautiful shells, a sharp Marlin Spike, delicately marked Olives and a gaggle of shining Cowries ranging from a large Leopard (a species which is surprisingly rare on the Chagos) to two tiny Isabellas, and one large but perfect Frog shell. The court suppressed a gasp of congratulation and even the Commander's fingers twitched beneath the table. There was the proof of one very successful 'grotting' expedition, but the Major stood his ground. He spoke, 'I beg the court's indulgence to consider two other exhibits.' A bland 'yes' sent the Major's hand to the table beside him. Two more hessian sacks one labelled P, the other Q, were emptied on to the table, each contained a diverse collection of corals ready for logging and enumeration. Charles Sheppard stepped forward as specialist witness, checked them against the official lists and pronounced, 'A perfect collection from the required depth.' The official photographer stepped forward with a roll of film still wet from the developing tank. Exposure No. 1 was of a dive board which bore 39/80/Q/P (Transect 38 Depth 80 feet Quadrat collection, Bag P).

The Court was adjourned. Major Lane left with the shells to begin the unsavoury part of the cleansing operation. Alan Baldwin cornered the Diving Officer to arrange an official Grotting dive on that site.

Fictitious as that scene may be it almost could have happened. Coral collecting, although great in diving terms, didn't have quite the same gleaming rewards as 'grotting' or, to be exact, collecting molluscs. The fact is that corals are not nearly as nice to look at as shells even though they are destined for the scientific collection. The finding of another sort of coral for the collection only stirred up the Scientificos. Finding a new shell was always greeted with enthusiasm by the whole expedition. So grotting was a popular pastime. To discover the elusive molluscs you have to 'grot' along the bottom, peering into, around and especially under things, hence the term.

There is no doubt that one of the best times for grotting is in the early morning when some of the night feeding forms may still be out on the crawl. This is especially true once the expedition has been under way for some weeks because the majority of the molluscs which are active by day will already be in the collection. There is also no doubt that the best habitat for 'grotting' is in sandy areas, especially those subjected to regular currents. Such places are the chosen home of two of the most sought-after shells, the Augers and the Olives, which wander about just beneath the surface of the sand, as they go leaving tell-tale trails not unlike moles. If you are lucky and go to the right end of the trail before your buddy then your mollusc may become the prize specimen of the day.

The other type of habitat preferred by the 'grotters' was known as a catastrophe strip. This was an area which for one reason or another was littered with dead corals. Of course grotting in such places was much harder work, necessitating the lifting of coral rock to search out the

Cowries are more beautiful when alive, aren't they?

sleeping Cowries and Cones. Each rock had then to be replaced so that our scientific endeavours caused as little disturbance as possible.

Every now and again special 'grots' were built into the dive programme, each led by Adrian and his number two, Gordon Raku. Grotting is a slow steady process and the team would always stay down for the absolute maximum safe time. Such dives were often accompanied by Raku's underwater 'singing' and although his repertoire was enormous you could always tell if he was in a good area because his tune changed to 'Bread of Heaven' and each descant of bubbles would tell of another find.

If there was any division between the diving members of the expedition it was into Grotters and Non-Grotters and the most satisfying thing which could happen to one of the latter was to discover an as yet unrecorded shell collected by accident with the coral by a Grotter. This was not a rare occurrence because one of the favourite habitats of the two-shelled molluscs (*Lamellibranchs*) is in holes in the coral rock.

Apart from the pretties with the hard outside there is another group of molluscs which every diver hopes to find, at least as long as they are not too big. This group includes the Squids and Octopuses. The former are a great rarity on a dive, mainly because many of them are pelagic and live out over very deep water. On a couple of occasions we were lucky enough to see them swimming by, tentacles first, out-stretched, sensing the water. To give chase was futile, the reward being no more than an exclamation mark of black ink and an empty seascape.

The Octopuses were a different matter, quite easy to find and not too difficult to capture. It was not unusual to meet one tip-tentacling after its prey around a coral head, or just sitting furling and unfurling its long appendages, one at a time much in the same way as we humans twiddle thumbs. As soon as the octopus realises that something unusual is present in its vicinity it instantly freezes in its tracks and begins to go through its complete colour and texture change repertoire which ends with its blending into the background, so as to be almost invisible.

The only real trouble about diving on the Chagos Bank is that there is just too much to see, let alone record. We had decided right from the start to limit our collections to the reef-forming Corals, and the Gorgonians, Molluscs and Echinoderms (Urchins, Starfish and the like), probably less than one per cent of the actual life of the reef. Even that limited objective kept us all hard at it and we consoled ourselves with the fact that we were studying the most important components of the reef. It was not really very much consolation because we knew that in a living community no one part is more important than the others. Without the continuous supply of microscopic animals and plants brought in on each tide the coral animals could not do their work. Likewise without the horde of scavengers and, in the main, unseen decomposers the waste products of the reef builders could accumulate and taint the whole system, bringing reef life to a standstill.

This is the true dynamic nature not only of the coral reef but of all natural living ecosystems. An ecosystem is one in which each member has a job or jobs to do and in which no single job can be said to be more important than others. In the same way the job of each member is always well done because if it is not that member will be replaced by something that will do it better, for this is the basic mechanism of evolution.

14.
The Hunting
of Gollum

The opportunity came to return to Egmont for a three-day stay. Perhaps it was just nostalgia, or to see if anyone had dared to visit our island or to ascertain whether the scars of our camp site had been erased by the sands of two years' time, I don't know, but I wanted to go. So it was that late one night we embarked on the *Four Friends* south to our old diving grounds. Until that time my only experience of the ketch in motion had been when it was under power and then, although I don't wish to be rude to a most elegant lady, she did tend to wallow a bit. Under sail she was a breathtaking experience, live as anything down on the reef below. The wind sang loud songs through her shrouds and even the baggy wrinkles filled out in their fullest splendour.

Not only does the ketch come alive when she is under sail, but so does Warren Blake. He stands caressing the wheel with seemingly gentle movements that are translated to the rudder via a hydraulic ram. Warren is not at the helm of his boat, he is a living part of her, the stresses and strains of wind and current reacting on the sails and the hull being transformed through his knowledge to the correct bearing by compass. Sailing on the high seas is a very different experience from my, till then limited, horizons of sailing the Norfolk Broads. There one leg of a tack could be as short as 50 yards; here in mid-ocean it could go on for 1,000 miles or indeed as long as the wind held out.

The wind was set fair for Egmont and the set of the mainsail hardly moved throughout the voyage. First light was welcomed by the engines spluttering into life to allow us to manoeuvre through the reef channel and into the shelter of the lagoon. Despite a slight altercation with one of the many coral heads we were soon at anchor in Boat Bay adjacent to the old settlement. Perhaps we were only just in time because the wind had been freshening throughout the voyage and was now beginning to gust in a rather ominous way. We were soon ashore, however, where we forgot about the wind.

Nothing had changed. The ruins of the settlement still crumbled among the palms; the rats ran in and out of the *Scaevola* and the usual pile of tidal debris lay on the beach. All was just as it should be. The short walk along to our camp site revealed four left-footed flip flops, three glass fishing floats still safe in their string bags, innumerable bits of coconut and three lovely Nautilus shells, water-washed but still resplendent in their orange markings.

The camp site had disappeared beneath a mantle of green leaves and the top of the tide line was edged with new *Scaevola*, most of it over 6 feet in height. The only thing to mark our seventy-two-day stay was a heap of rusty sand where our last fire had been dowsed in haste and Chuggles' tower protruding up into the branches of the Hibiscus tree on which two Fairy Terns were taking turns to guard their egg.

Mont and I turned our backs on the camp site and made our way down the seaward length of Île Sudest. Coconut crabs peered out from their lairs in among the jumbled mass of roots. The El Maren Monument had mellowed and looked as if it had been in position since 1920; everything was perfect.

But one thing was changed. The barachois were much lower in water than they had been on our last visit, strange because this time we were in the height of the rainy season. Lying along the edge of the diminishing pools were three gigantic Milkfish, not long dead because the hordes of hermit crab were only just gathering for the feast. The Serpentine barachois was even drier, and the smell and serried ranks of skeletons were in places the only proof that water had been present.

This is your life cycle, the masked Boobys of Resurgent.

The small pool of water that was left was choc-a-bloc full of the sleek Milkfish, their dorsal fins, like flotillas of sharks, stood clear of the water. Rain must come and come soon or else all the fish would die.

It was good to be back and stand while the warm bacterial ooze bubbled up between your toes and the familiar smell of hydrogen sulphide permeated the air. Looking out towards the sea, we saw something else very wrong. Five large trees lifted green needle-like leaves up towards the sky. They were *Casuarina*, the curse of the natural vegetation of tropical islands. They had not been there before? Our records showed that they had, but then they were much smaller. I could in fact remember Mont standing on that very spot two years earlier hotly debating the pros and cons of removing them.

The trouble with *Casuarina* is that it has roots which contain bacteria that can fix nitrogen from the air. This gives it an unfair advantage over the majority of the other members of the flora and hence it acts as a very pugnacious weed. Once it has a foothold in an island system there is very little that can be done to bring it under control. If only we had removed the seedlings. We scouted round and found seven new saplings which we pulled up and sank in the sea, and decided that tomorrow we would remove the parents.

It was getting late and we had to head back to the ketch. Below the offending *Casuarina*, the *Scaevola* dipped down into the barachois and as we stepped into the water a snake-like form with what looked like two external gills slid off into the gloom. It was the mystery animal that we had sighted only once during the whole of the last expedition and had since that time wondered if it had been a figment of our imaginations. Two, no three more glided out to join the first, now busily feeding on the bacterial detritus just a few feet away. The mystery was partly solved; whatever it was shunned the bright sun and only came out to feed in the evening. We christened our four new friends *Gollum gollum*, decided that we must catch one, and headed back to the ketch.

On board it was a night for celebration. For some of us it was our return, for the others their first footing on a new island. Egmont fish *à la* Tue washed down with McEwan's beer began it all and Glenmorangie malt scotch finished it off, bringing the party to the full realisation that what had to be done should not be put off until tomor-

Casuarina, alien on the Egmont skyline — an intruder with a problem in its roots.

row. The hunting of *Gollum* was on. The wind was still rising, but the night was clear, with all the stars of the equatorial heavens vying with a pale yellow moon. Nets, torches and buckets were noisily gathered together and the whole happy party took to the boats for the short paddle to shore. It was a low tide and so the boat journey took us only to the edge of the deep anchorage. The sand was in pristine condition, unmarked by the feet of man after whatever day of the week he is named, but not for long. Eight sets of tracks raced along the beach picking their way among the coral debris and funnelling into the gap in the *Scaevola* that marked the entrance to the barachois.

The hunting party was not in what could be called a quiet mood and great hilarity greeted every palm frond as we crackled our way through the coconut grove. Emerging into the open, all members donned footwear to flip flop their way across the reef of fish bones. The scene was set, the surface of the water mirrored black as we all stood at the ready, 'Boots' with a bucket, Warren with a net, the rest of us ready to act as beaters.

Pandemonium on the left flank as several hundred Milkfish took off in front of the line. False alarm. We all stood still and began to sink into the warm rich ooze that formed the bottom of the pond. Quietly,

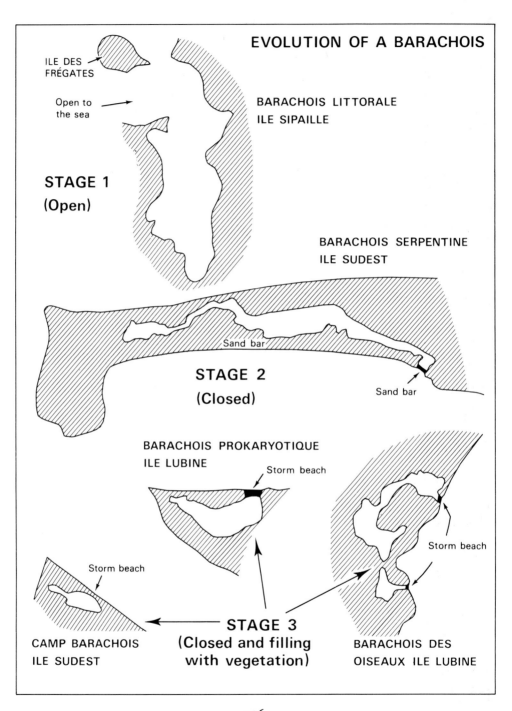

EVOLUTION OF A BAROCHOIS

ILE DES FRÉGATES

Open to the sea →

BAROCHOIS LITTORALE
ILE SIPAILLE

STAGE 1
(Open)

BAROCHOIS SERPENTINE
ILE SUDEST

Sand bar

STAGE 2
(Closed)

Sand bar

BAROCHOIS PROKARYOTIQUE
ILE LUBINE

Storm beach

Storm beach

Storm beach

CAMP BAROCHOIS
ILE SUDEST

STAGE 3
(Closed and filling
with vegetation)

BAROCHOIS DES
OISEAUX ILE LUBINE

but firmly, Dave Young's voice said, 'Here's one'. The net was quickly passed along down the line of emergent beaters now all firmly trapped by clinging bacteria. Swish! 'Got it', a triumphant shout broke the warm silence. Then everyone moved in with dark sucking plops to see the captive, but before the lid could be snapped on to the bucket *Gollum* shot vertically upwards out of the bucket in a desperate bid for freedom; not for long. Everyone who hadn't already fallen over leapt to the rescue, as bucket and net scooped up gallons of goo and several very surprised Milkfish.

Although *Gollum* was re-enmeshed in the net several times, each time he got away, finally to be lost in the sea of mud, water, palm leaves and intrepid hunters. We withdrew to the bank to consider a new strategy.

A line of beaters, net and bucket in the centre, were deployed across the lake, the idea being to turn our next quarry into the trap set in the middle. We progressed forward, sinking deeper and deeper into the warm mud and herding the Milkfish as we went. Several Gollums were sighted, but they found it a simple matter to break through our slimy ranks. The hunt had by now lasted well over one hour and blood, alcohol and enthusiasm were beginning to wane. Suddenly we realised that Warren was missing from the line. Had he sunk into the 'mire'? Torchlight soon picked him out squatting on the edge of the lake working on a short piece of chicken wire. Soon the Blake Mark I Gollum Trap was complete and two minutes later we had caught one ready for the bucket.

Those external gills were not gills at all but elongated pectoral fins. *Gollum* was an eel; the mystery was solved and the whole party broke out into a victory dance.

Next morning the re-survey was completed and the four offending *Casuarinas* together with all seedlings were removed. The skyline of Barachois Serpentine was back in its original state, the pernicious tree removed from the flora of Egmont.

The wind had by now freshened to about force 6, unfortunately in exactly the wrong direction, and as we were in a hurry it was going to have to be motor all the way and a rough ride back to Eagle.

Ketches are designed to move under sail and the *Four Friends* is no

Gollum the eel, native home Barachois Serpentine. Egmont, Central Indian Ocean.

exception, so it was not her fault that she made heavy going against the enormous mass of waves. From your position in the cockpit it was easy to get firsthand knowledge of the ways in which waves are generated. The wind whips up the surface of the water into a mass of tiny wavelets all rushing in different directions, bumping into each other and dissipating their energy. However during their brief existence, the wind can get behind their diminutive crests adding more energy and beginning to build up real rolling water. The area of sea over which this process of wave building takes place is called the Generation Area. There was little doubt that we were heading into a very large Generation Area. For the first time in the whole expedition I was glad of my layer of insulation fat (although already somewhat diminished) to keep me warm, as sheets of green water flooded into the cockpit. Passing close along the lee shore of Danger Island, we were able to check our future landing spot, although landing in weather like that would have been completely out of the question. There lay our main objective, ringed by massive surf, an island called Danger.

None too soon our voyage came to an end as the tops of Eagle Island's palms came into view above the spray and the local inhabitants came down to meet us.

During our absence the dive parties had not been idle and shining examples of coral ready for the pristine collection were bleaching in the warm after-storm sunshine.

15.
A Hundred Inches of Rain

Harry Carden is, or rather until St. Valentine's Day 1975 was, a member of the Army Catering Corps. His career in this the most important part of any marching army had been far removed from the accepted bangers and beans routine. As sometime chef to the Duchess of Kent and to General Maugham, his expertise echoed in the halls of the famous pastry cooks and confectioners. His artistry had been woven into one of the official wedding cakes of no less a personage than Mrs. Mark Phillips and his job on the expedition was to weld, if that is the right word, a series of appetising meals from the golden cans of compo. Singed bacon grill con gallons of chili sauce were things of the last expedition. Most days the smell of new-baked bread wafted from the cook tent tempting all loafers within range of Harry's meat cleaver, and every evening the range of dishes was awaited with aching salivary glands. Fish added the touch of perfection to the variety of compo menus, and there were only grumbles when it came round once more to Chicken Supreme.

Harry is a staunch believer in good positive cooking with a dash of rum and coke for inspiration, and thanks to his trojan service in the heat of the calor stoves, the expedition marched, swathed and dived on its stomach.

Apart from his culinary performances, his other duty was as met man and tide-gauge operator. A shiny copper rain gauge shone in brighter splendour than any of his cooking pots and every day at 09.00

hours Zulu, which was in fact 14.00 Eagle, the day's rainfall had to be measured with care and all the other gadgets had to be seen to. These included a daily whirl with the whirling hygrometer that told us that the humidity was always very high, usually above 95 per cent, changing the chart on the recording tide gauge, that told us the relative position of both sun and moon, a quick rewind job and then back to design the next evening meal.

Over the period of our stay the tide went in and out the regulation 122 times with a maximum amplitude of 91 inches. This, the highest tide, washed right up into the camp site, undermining some of the local coconuts to such an extent that they began to die, shedding both leaves and fruits straight down upon the camp beneath.

Despite certain Canute-like characteristics of the tide gauge, which used to get stuck when full out, the pattern of readings was kept up for one complete month, enough to provide data to be added to the next edition of the Tide Tables for the Central Indian Ocean. The pattern of rainfall likewise behaved itself, giving a very similar sort of record to that on Diego Garcia over the same period. It is thus possible to extrapolate our total readings to cover the whole year, giving an annual total of around 100 inches. This means that every square yard of the island would receive about 500 gallons of fresh water each year, making a total of 12 billion gallons for the whole catchment. Some of this must evaporate away almost immediately while the rest, sinking into the porous sand, supplies the vegetation with all its watery needs, and recharges the reservoir of sweet water down in the coral rock.

The air photographs revealed the presence of two small open 'pools' near the southern end of the island. One of them was bone dry, a fact which was difficult to explain for we had planned our stay for the rainy season. The other, though much diminished in size, was overflowing with Milkfish.

Apart from these two blanks in the general order of the coconuttery, many other patterns including more or less open spaces showed up on the black and white print. We thus found it possible to walk the entire length of the island almost unhindered and although it was a somewhat tortuous route, it was christened 'the main drag'. The bulk of the main drag is a ridge like a hog's back, which runs along much of the island,

and survey showed that it rises to more than 5 feet above spring high water mark. In an attempt to counteract the effects of this rise which results in the water-table being further and further from the surface, each coconut had been planted in a saucer-shaped depression cut into the rock, the higher up on the ridge the deeper the palm 'pot', and on the highest part of the ridge even the deepest excavations had failed to keep their palms supplied with their daily needs, for many stood empty.

The many 'pots' which still held palms down on the lower levels were each full of cast fronds and innumerable coconuts which had sprouted their vigorous seedlings. The majority of the young palms were however dead, for in competition with their deeper-rooting parents they had little chance to obtain water in the height of the dry season. One other factor of importance in the demise of the coconuts were scuttling around under the piles of part rotten fronds. Rats were everywhere and the easiest way to catch one or two was to creep up to a fallen coconut, approaching its pointed end, and then quickly turn it flat end down thus trapping the rats feasting inside. The likelihood of a coconut bouncing and rolling into one of the unoccupied 'pots' and then escaping the ravening horde of rats was unlikely; and hence regeneration of the palms is severely limited.

Wherever the copra farmers had left other trees within the plantations, probably to provide the workers with some shade for the midday rest period, things were very different. Perhaps the rats were so fond of coconuts that they left the fruits of the other trees alone, or perhaps the other trees were better able to overcome the other problems of island life. Whatever the reason, around most of the broad-leaved trees there were hundreds of healthy seedlings and saplings, and everywhere the broad-leaved trees certainly appeared to be making a very positive comeback at the expense of the palms.

The main drag runs close to the western edge of the island and it was quite easy to locate it from any point along that shore. East of the ridge was a very different place and it soon came to be known as the badlands, a depression or rather a series of depressions, the floor of which was below high water mark, being protected from inundation only by a storm beach or perhaps it was a second hog's back of lesser proportion

Palm Pot carved in the
rock in the hope of copra
to come.

The ever so English
Typha swamp, to me the
making of a perfect
paradise.

Lumnitzera racemosa, a most way out mangrove, the only one that grows in the middle of the Indian Ocean.

If you lived in thick mud and could breathe through your knees, you would stick them up into the fresh air. Breathing knee roots of *Lumnitzera racemosa.*

situated close to the eastern shore.

If you wanted to get lost on Eagle, this was the place in which to do it, an expanse of tall plantation with well-spaced palms protruding from thick scrub and in places waist deep in ferns. The ground was wet and spongy underfoot, the vegetation festooned with spiders' webs and the air full of gnats, not at all the place in which to have to work.

On our second encounter with the badlands I was stumbling about with Mont completely lost and looking for a way out, when all of a sudden I found myself standing in the open alongside a very familiar plant, a Reed Mace (Bull Rush to some) complete with flower head. I remember pinching myself to ascertain that I was awake and not dreaming, I asked Mont for confirmation of the fact and when he replied, proving that I was awake, my amazement increased.

Much as I like coral reefs and especially atolls, the first love in my botanical life is a peat bog or mire. Here we were on an atoll in the Central Indian Ocean and we were standing on the edge of a mire! To me this was absolute heaven despite the gnats which were busy gnawing at my extremities. Reed Mace, and Spike Rush in abundance made us feel more than at home. The only other dominant plant was a grass which refused to come into flower throughout the whole of our stay and therefore remained unidentified.

We traced the mire along behind the settlement where it lost itself in dense woodland of Hibiscus, but not for long; the ground soon became wet underfoot once more and there, protruding from the saturated peat, were the unmistakable knee roots of a Mangrove, *Lumnitzera racemosa*.

Mangroves are found throughout the tropics and wherever sea meets land they help to form a protective barrier between the salt and fresh-water. Living in waterlogged conditions they have become adapted to the lack of oxygen around their nether parts by the development of special 'breathing' roots which grow up above soil level. This adaptation has been their key to success in this very harsh environment and has given them the freedom of the tropical world. Our find had certainly endorsed this fact, for up to that moment there had been one large gap in their worldwide distribution and that was the Central Indian Ocean. Now it was filled.

The mangrove swamp was itself very extensive and we spent many hours surveying its boundaries and probing its mysteries. In the past it had been connected to the sea via at least two openings which were now closed off by storm beaches, although during the periods of extra high tide and onshore winds some overspill of sea water did take place. There was little doubt that the mire and the mangrove had developed in old barachois.

Many facts began to fit together as the secrets of this tropical mire complex were unravelled. There has always been some doubt in the literature concerning the exact method of formation of barachois. Those first described from Diego Garcia are all connected to the sea and proof of the fact is easily obtained simply by tasting the water.

All the barachois we found on the islands of the Chagos Bank were cut off from the sea, their waters being at least semi-sweet, that is all except Barachois Littorale on Île Sipaille in the Egmont Group. This is an elongated horseshoe of bare white sand at low tide and an area of milky tepid water when the tide is in. It is devoid of vegetation and the only signs of permanent life are the conical mounds of the burrowing crab *Cardiosoma*. Its visitors are more diverse and include a full range of the islands' migrant birds stomping about in the shallows or picking their delicate ways between the tidal influx of Sting Rays and an abundance of Milkfish.

It is quite an easy matter to imagine how the mouth of such an embayment could be closed off by a storm beach or sand bar. The enclosed water body would thus be left to the ravages of time without tide but with an influx of more than 100 inches of rain each year. Salt water could in this way soon be replaced by fresh.

The Serpentine barachois on Sudest could well have been formed since the visit of Captain Moresby. His map shows two islands, Sudest and Tattamucca, joined by a sand bar. Now the two islands appear welded into one by two parallel bars of sand and shingle within which an area that was once within the upper tidal range is now full of sweet water and Milkfish. It seems likely that the ancestors of the contemporary Milkfish horde got cut off in the process and have since prospered in their new-found isolation.

All the other barachois lie behind storm beaches and yet in each case it is possible to trace what may have been their connection to the sea. They are now shut off from the direct influence of sea water (except in periods of exceptionally bad weather) by a hydrostatic lock mechanism acting in the porous sand and rock. Their volumes are however all affected by the twice daily excursions of the tide, presumably due to changes of pressure as the tide goes in and out. During periods of extreme low tide it was not an unusual thing to find rills of fresh water bubbling from the storm beaches to lose themselves in among masses of pink bacteria and red seaweeds that encrust the rocks of the upper tidal range.

The flora of the 'fresh water' barachois is the most bizarre of all. It consists of a mat of algae and bacteria which has some very remarkable properties. The mat may be as much as 2 feet thick and its surface is covered by a weft of blue-green algal filaments which not only photosynthesise, producing oxygen as a by-product of energy fixation, but they also have the ability of fixing atmospheric nitrogen into a utilisable form.

In this way the surface film of plants not only keeps the whole living mat supplied with much of the energy it requires, but produces nitrogen fertiliser exactly where it is wanted, and keeps the surface waters saturated with oxygen throughout the daylight hours. However, just below this all-action surface film which was often covered with bubbles of pure oxygen, there is a dark and very different world. Below the algae is a thick wodge of bacteria, often of a rich plum red colour, living it down in a habitat that is almost devoid of oxygen. Here exist a whole range of bacteria, most of which depend upon organic matter which falls from the 'table' of the upper algal mat, and a by-product of this anaerobic world is the gas hydrogen sulphide, the bane of the island's water supply. Apart from the all-pervading aroma of bad eggs, the H_2S made its presence felt in a very unusual way. Evidently in time pockets of the gas get trapped underneath the mat, so much so that the pressure builds up, fracturing the sandwich and erupting to the surface. The result is even more H_2S in the air, what looks like gigantic footprints on the floor of the barachois and a surfeit of energy-rich detritus floating about on the surface ready for the hungry Milkfish. In essence the barachois of the Chagos Bank appear to be perfect self-charging fish farms, the only real imperfection being the smell.

Anything which falls into one of these ponds is scheduled for very rapid destruction unless it has a tough protective coat and sinks very quickly down into the anaerobic layer. Now it just happens that the pollen grains and the spores of many plants are covered with a tough coat which is very resistant to decay. What is more many of these coats are textured and sculptured in such a way that they may be recognised and identified, at least by an expert.

Each year some of the myriad of pollen grains produced by the plants on the islands must fall into the barachois and some will get into the anaerobic layer where they will remain waiting for the light of the expert.

All this is only the beginning of the story, for our finds on Eagle Island show that given time and moderately stable conditions the barachois eventually become partly filled with the bacterial ooze, on which other plants begin to grow, producing a mire or a mangrove swamp and gradually turning the open water into semi-dry land.

The facts all begin to fit and some unfortunately have done so only in retrospect. Mires and mangroves are only present on Eagle Island, but senescent barachois, covered in part by coconut plantations and damp forest, were present both on Eagle and South Brother. On the latter island the area of the old barachois was a most fantastic place, being covered by a dense thicket of *Alocasia macrorhiza*, an aroid, or kind of arum, looking something like giant rhubarb. Many of the plants were over 12 feet in height, an almost impenetrable mass of succulent leaf stalks. They were growing on a dark peat of around 2 feet in thickness, developed over the algal bacterial deposits so typical of the open barachois. A detailed study of all the old barachois of Eagle was put into full swing and samples of all the layers from the surface peat down to the sand beneath were taken for subsequent analysis.

Preliminary study of these samples has shown that coconut pollen is present only in the top 3 inches of the deposit and below this there is pollen of a range of the trees now present on the island and some mystery grains which have not as yet been identified. The samples await full analysis and when complete this should provide us with an insight into the make-up of the vegetation that existed on the islands

Tropical peat, a profile of the history not only of a barachois but of an island.

Buttress roots, sure signs ▶ of a rainy climate and poorly drained soils in the tropics.

Alocasia macrorhiza grown for food and now running wild especially on the wetter soils.

before man introduced his coconuts and his rats.

It was while working on the laboratory analysis of the peat that a thought suddenly struck me. Why had I not thought of it while we were still within sailing distance of Egmont? In among the more natural areas of the forests of Île Sudest there were some areas damp underfoot and picked out by the presence of a few plants of *Alocasia macrorhiza*. We had spent a lot of time studying the vegetation of the area because it was dominated by trees with buttress roots. Buttress roots are typical of trees growing in tropical rain forest, their function being without doubt to prop up the massive trees which, growing in a very damp climate and hence continuously wet soil, cannot put their roots down very far because of lack of oxygen. Could the buttress-rooted forests of Egmont indeed be growing on the remains of an old barachois? I just don't know, but what I do know is that a coral atoll developed in an area subject to 100 inches of rain each year is a paradise for both a diver and a peatnick.

Having said all that, it must be concluded that interesting as the senescent barachois may be they provide no evidence to dispute the other theory of formation by erosion. Comparison of the Moresby and Phillips maps of Egmont show that the atoll is undergoing a massive series of changes through the agencies of both erosion and accretion, the *status quo* being a quasi-balance between the two. Both theories about the origin of barachois may be valid in different situations.

If this is so, it poses two interesting questions. First, what are the pincer-like spurs on the lagoonward side of the Moresby map of Egmont? Are they the first or last stages of barachois formation or breakdown? Second and perhaps more important, if the 'cofferdam' false reef across the entrance to the lagoon continues to grow upwards in unison with the reef front, could a new island be formed together with a ready-made barachois?

16.
The Secrets
of Nelson

News came that the B.B.C. team would join the expedition through Gan rather than via Colombo as originally planned. This meant that the ketch did not have to leave to pick them up until 13th February, giving the main expedition an extra ten days of sail time. So Plan Nelson swung into feverish action.

Way up north on the main ring of the Chagos Bank one other tiny scrap of land was shown on the charts; its name is Nelson. Records state that it was occasionally visited by people from nearby Peros Banhos and the Salomons in order to collect birds' eggs to vary their staple diets of fish and coconut. Now this statement alone was enough to get Mont's primary feathers up, especially as a visit of about one hour's duration by one John Frazier a few years previously had reported a hut and many nesting birds. Now we had the opportunity of a short visit and the challenge to gather as much information as possible during the time, so that by the end of the expedition our report would cover all the islands of the Chagos Bank.

The plan was to drop the main diving party on Middle Brother to continue the underwater work and then to make a quick dash across the Bank to Nelson. The afternoon of the start was as calm as could be, with not enough wind to ruffle a Frigate's feather and so it was engines full ahead and Nelson here we come. The main party was duly landed and with comments of 'Bloody millionaires, swanning it around the Indian Ocean!' we set motor to cross the hidden bank.

Shades of Salomon's
prosperous past: labourers'
huts empty and starting
to decay.

A barachois still showing
its marine connection.

The pattern has changed,
erosion is rife, the
Scaevola has gone and the
next line of defence
Guettardia speciosa is
dead.

Navigation is a craft, rather than a science and, like all crafts, long apprenticeship is the only way to learn, for courses, however well plotted on the chart, can go sadly awry in the teeth of currents unknown and a slight change in the wind. The first watch was easy; there were stars to aim at or rather between – those two to port, that one to starboard. Keep it like that and you were dead on course; no need for a compass. No sooner said than in rolled the clouds. The friendly firmament disappeared from view, leaving you with only the dim phosphorescence of a swinging compass to steer by. It is the same problem when driving a car at speed; if you keep your eyes way ahead it is quite easy to drive a straight course but look at the kerb just in front of the car and it is a great strain to do the same.

Out in mid-Bank there are however a whole series of sub-surface signposts in the form of hidden shoals and reefs, which bring the needle on the echo-sounder roaring up the face of the dial. However good you reckon you are at plotting and steering a course it is nice to know that the invisible echo is there, listening, feeling out the way, reading the Bank in electronic braille and every now and again letting you know that you are on course.

No bottom at 30 fathoms meant that we were over the deep water of the open lagoon. Our first marker was round about the half-way mark, a line of submerged reefs with ample water above them for safe passage and providing ample warning to alter course for Nelson. Clouds had now completely closed the heavens, and neither star nor planet shone to guide us. The shallower water appeared well ahead of schedule indicating that we had probably been riding a current that was hurrying us on our way. Somewhere ahead in the 180° of blackness lay our objective. Parallel rulers paced their way across the chart and Warren's experience laid out our new course. The hydraulics creaked as the *Four Friends* eased round towards the next point of reference in the jumble of Captain Moresby's braille. The appointed time of contact came and passed; that current had carried us further than estimated. Three short dog legs soon located the shallows and a new course was set. As the sun began to rise into a grey misty dawn so did Nelson, a pinprick with palms dead ahead on the horizon. 06.00 hours saw us lying off and eating a hearty breakfast before disembarkation. We now had around nine hours of daylight in which to discover the secrets of Nelson.

Landing was too easy; a deep channel led the inflatable into a lagoon sheltered by the reef front which flanked the seaward side. The island is shaped like a dumb-bell, the two ends consisting of coral rock connected by a broad spit of rock and sand. One main group of coconut palms is situated about half-way along the spit, apart from which few plants stood proud of the general lawn of scrub which appeared to cover much of the island. The closer we got, the more uniform did this scrub layer appear to be, the bulk of it *Scaevola* topiaried into order by seaspray and wind. A narrow ribbon of *Tournefortia* separated the *Scaevola* from the sea in many places and, standing in among the stunted bushes of this grey protective hedge, it was easy to see that the uniform lawn of scrub was not so uniform. Here and there larger bushes broke the surface contour, each one a focal centre for what we now thought of as the Chagos Booby, the Red Foots, together with juvenile Frigates. Up above the island the spiralling parents resplendent with white shirt front that ended in a straight line breast bone high told us that they were Greater Frigates. We had expected these birds to be in residence, for their nesting presence had been reported way back in the 1880s. But where were the profusion of birds which tempted the egg collectors to make the journey across from the copra plantations? From the sea there had been plenty of tern activity, but from our landing-place on the middle of the island we could see no nests at all. However, as soon as we began to walk towards one of the rocky ends of the island, up went the terns, thousands and thousands of them. Short stout beaks signified Greater Noddies and it wasn't difficult to find their nests. The rock above high water mark was littered with their buff-coloured eggs, each with a few darker spots. Nests they were not, but nest sites they undoubtedly were and the favourite spots appeared to be in the shade of the low bushes that dotted the shore. By now the sun was well and truly up and it was hot work beating the bounds of the ternery, and it soon became evident that the whole of the outer edge of Nelson was just that. Laying out a tape, we tried to count the eggs. From the outside we could easily see there was an egg per yard, but when we laid a series of tapes at right angles to the shore we just had to bump up the estimate to at least five

For key see page 104

eggs for every yard of shoreline. That was not all; odd colonies sent up worried parents from well inland wherever there was a clearer patch in among the scrub.

Eggs galore, thousands upon thousands, some fresh laid, and many not so fresh. Some were cracking while others were already balls of feathers 'snarling' at the intrusion of the camera down into their two-inch world.

The fringe of Noddy eggs went down to extreme high water mark, or very nearly. Between the last of the buff eggs and the water there was often a fringe of broken coral rock fretted by erosion and with some slabs piled into jumbled cairns by the force of high waves. This zone appeared to be shunned by the Noddies, and who could blame them, but here and there was a white egg speckled with orange brown and very reminiscent of the one found on the mini cliffs of Little Brother. We photographed and measured. What could they be? Surely we must soon find an adult bird.

We continued our circumnavigation of the island, counting and noting, completely oblivious of the fact that the time was roaring along. The strandline was littered with all the flotsam we had come to expect and lot more besides. Our best find was a skeleton of ribs and spars all made of best oak and pinned together by flat-headed copper nails with one copper-lifting shackle still firmly in place. A boat from some perhaps ill-fated ship? Detailed search revealed some other bits and pieces, but that was all.

In marked contrast to this relic of seafaring were two halves of a plastic life-raft case marked with Japanese script. They lay like some forgotten dinosaur's eggs, half buried in the sand and nearby were the remains of a rough shelter constructed of palm fronds, a pile of plastic containers labelled *Fuji Mineralwater* and a pile of assorted survival rations. Had it been a recent shipwreck? Or just an onshore party making clandestine use of a life-raft? Several empty bottles of Japanese whisky suggested the latter, but if so, why the rough shelter and survival rations? Here was another mystery of Nelson, but, however mysterious, the water in the hermetically sealed bottles was absolutely fabulous.

The isolated clump of palms first seen during our approach stood almost in the centre of the sandy neck which joined the two ends of the islands and there were other smaller groups on each of the 'bells'. These provided the only shade on the island and although our thirsts were well slaked thanks to the Fujiwater, it was good to get out of the sun. Within these arbours of shade the air was whirring with terns which fluttered around us like large inquisitive moths, uttering shrill cries. All the birds in the palms were Lesser, not Greater, Noddies, being readily distinguished by their sleeker heads and thinner longer bills. The palms were simply bursting with these delightful birds; one modest-sized tree sported twenty-two occupied nests on which the adults would sit tight for close-up photography. This was Lesser Noddy Land and apart from a few more isolated colonies, always on dead *Tournefortia* bushes, the rest of the island was the domain of the Greater of these fantastic Terns.

Continued survey around the edge of the island revealed a do-it-yourself fully interlocking Dolphin Skeleton Kit, all parts guaranteed present, as long as you had sufficient time to find them. It was during the search for the Dolphin's skull that we solved our number one mystery.

Protruding from a cavity beneath an untidy heap of coral rock were the tail feathers of a bird. As I approached it didn't take off, but simply retreated further in the confines of its hole. It was too easy to reach in and catch the mystery bird of Nelson and Little Brother. It was a Bridled Tern complete with bridled chick. Both were duly photographed and returned to their hole in which were the remains of one of the green speckled eggs.

We then began the task of counting all of these special nest sites present on the rim of the island and the total came to a mere seventeen. There seems little doubt that selection of such a specialised and restricted habitat must severely limit the success of these Terns, although it is possible that on other islands where the density of Noddy Terns is less, that the Bridled Tern may be able to make use of more extensive areas for nesting. However the fact that before our discovery there were only two doubtful records for this bird in the central Indian Ocean points to its rarity, at least in this neck of the seas.

The afternoon was long and hot and many trips were made to the cache of Fuji water, each bottle of which bore on its label a picture of that famous volcano, a scene as different from Nelson Island as it is possible to envisage. Yet is it? Below the coral rock which now forms the home of these myriads of birds there are great pillars of basalt, proof of the gigantic volcanism of past ages which helped push the floating continent apart, producing the Indian Ocean. This is a process which may well still be going on, and we had been given a sharp reminder of the fact earlier on in the expedition. We had all been sitting in the mess tent on the evening of 29th January when the lamps began to sway quite violently along with the tent poles and even the great palms outside. Undoubtedly these were the surface manifestation of some seismic activity, an earthquake or eruption, perhaps deep down at the base of the Bank, and on two other occasions much less severe tremors were felt, both on Eagle Island.

Late in the afternoon a dive was organised close to the mouth of the lagoon channel where the reef front sloped at an angle of about $25°$ down to a depth of 20 feet. This gently shelving portion of the reef front was fluted in the furrow and groove pattern so typical of partially exposed reef fronts. From the 20-foot mark the reef front plunged vertically away; on and just below the edge of this drop off a great variety of fish were amassed, each playing its own game of peek-a-boo, rushing back into the shelter of its own particular coral head. The reason for their wary behaviour was all too obvious, for not far below the blue space was boiling with predators. Most conspicuous among them were black and grey Groupers each about the size of a dustbin and ready for a meal of any size, and there marauding in the milk-blue mid-distance a school of Barracuda, some thousand strong interspersed with a variety of medium shark. It was a good place in which to be able to feel the protective wall of the reef against your back. At around the 40-foot mark there were a series of shallow recesses, not caves in the strict sense but places in which the reef had slumped away, sending slabs of rock cascading into the depths. Each recess was the castle of a large Grouper, most of which appeared to skulk almost 'asleep' in the darkest corner, where, although the light intensity was still quite good, it was dark enough to allow some of the deep water life forms to grow. It was while returning from one of these Grouper lairs that Warren and Tue added yet another mystery to Nelson's column. There poised on the lip of the cliff was a large anchor, welded by lime and time in the position in which it had perhaps become irretrievably stuck when some ship tried to up anchor and away.

Wild flights of sub-aqua fantasy tried to link the anchor with the skeleton of the ship's boat. The pattern of the two artefacts certainly pointed to a similar period. Our time on Nelson was up, however, so we left the anchor and its mystery where it was and the clouds of fish closed in around the iron flukes as if to laugh at those lesser souls who need an anchor to survive in the surf above their reef.

Early next morning we left Nelson in search of Victory Bank, a completely submerged reef of some 300 acres in extent. An hour and a quarter north out from Nelson Victory was in sight, a patch of light green reflection in the deep blue sea. We set our course straight across the centre and timed the run, all eyes on the flickering needle as the echo-sounder read out the message in braille. Translated it told of a submerged atoll, its rim some 21 feet below the surface, with a central lagoon shelving to a depth of more than 210 feet. Apart from the difference in the colour of the sea around the Bank, the area was full of life and the ketch gave inadvertent chase to a school of Dolphins as we left its northern rim. They somersaulted their way through the water just ahead of the boat, arching up to flare in the sunlight and then back through their own hurl of foam. As they went they performed victory rolls, in apt tribute to their habitat. What was Victory Bank like underwater? One day we must return to find out; but now we had more pressing work to do.

Out of the uncertainty of the zone of refraction, that is the air-sea interface when seen from a distance, the shapes of palms came unsteadily into view. At first there were three main clumps, and as the engines pushed us forward these gradually metamorphosed into three of the long low islands of the atoll called Salomon. The messages found by the advance party on Peros Banhos had told us that the settlement on Salomon had been closed down only a few years earlier. So as we negotiated the channel in towards the jostle of roofs, we expected no rush of locals to greet our arrival. The coconut farmers who had fed so well on the eggs from Nelson were no more, and the only welcome came from a large Fish Eagle which lifted its measured weight from off the water to perch just where a Fish Eagle should perch, on an old marker post standing alone marking the edge of the deep-water channel.

The settlement was silent, shimmering in the heat of a perfect day. From the short jetty a railway track curved back to skirt a gigantic Rose Tree ringed with benches, and then bifurcated to the various parts of the copra conurbation. The trucks were still on the tracks and although the points were overgrown with the tenacity of Morning Glory they were still in working order so the more mechanically minded section of the party could play at 'real' trains. Between the Rose Tree and the only two-storeyed house, there stood a pair of copra presses. They consisted of a large iron mortar with a palm trunk for a pestle, each of which was joined to a gigantic wooden beam about twice the size of a railway sleeper. At the extremity of this massive beam was a rather pitiful circular track worn deep in the coral sand, pitiful because we knew that the force which motivated this horizontal treadmill had been donkey power. To prove it there were three small sets of harness made of sacking and ropes, in a pile in the corner of the main store shed. All around the settlement there was fresh donkey spoor and although we didn't actually see one, at least their braying in the distance told us that they were there enjoying a more restful retirement.

The houses ranged from the two-storeyed wooden structure with a shingled roof, the abode of the manager, down through those of the lesser officials. The pecking order was indicated by the area of corrugated iron roof, the workers' huts being protected only by coconut leaves. Each house and hut had a character of its own and all that was missing were the cries of the children at play. In the gardens the weeds had taken over and only the tallest of the cultivated plants still survived. Plants like Alocasia, the gigantic arum, some of which were complete with their large lurid yellow bracts hiding the flowers, grew together with Breadfruit and Limes, so it was all hands to collect fresh fruit.

One of the smaller leaf-thatched huts was a regular Fort Knox, being surrounded by a high corrugated iron fence. Protruding above the perimeter defences were tufts of gigantic undivided leaves, from the centre of which drooped the unmistakable male flower of the banana, above each of which in ordered hands were great tassels of green fingers. Without its owner, Fort Knox soon gave up its treasures, which although unripe were full of succulent promise.

Although the life of the island's children may well have revolved around the yellow fruits of Fort Knox, the island life itself must have revolved around its church. It now stood silent and empty, a substantial building cool in its thickness of coral rock. The disordered rows of pews and ornately carved confessional were flecked with the colours of one simple circlet of stained glass.

The other main feature of this human habitation were the neat wells dotted throughout the area, each one capped with concrete and most closed by a wooden trap door designed to stop things, especially rats, from falling in. Wherever there was a roof of corrugated iron or better, intricate systems of gutters were in place to lead the precious rain water into large storage tanks, which in the absence of permanent residents were full to overflowing. Our last act before taking our leave of Salomon was to take a long cold shower full of soap suds and devoid of hydrogen sulphide. All the gear and fresh fruit was loaded on to a railway truck and the points were set for the end of the jetty.

Why had we come to Salomon – not just for fruit and a bath? No, we came to check up on the rat position (they were there and in abundance) and also to check on the settlement; it was all there and in working order, a perfect base camp for the future.

Our half-holiday was over; we basked in our new-found cleanliness and another of Tue's memorable meals with Ohio shortcake washed down with fresh limejuice made the Vietnamese way. (One fresh ripe lime squeezed into a half pint tumbler of water, add sugar to taste, and enjoy it.)

Darkness came and with it night, for evening has no real meaning under the equator. The sky was clouded black except for a fountain of stars which sprayed up to the apex of the heavens. We now had to negotiate the channel out through the reef; fortunately it was a straight course and bearings had been carefully checked before the light had gone. The anchor was weighed, all torches being kept away from the helmsman's eyes, for any sudden flash of light can ruin night vision for as long as twenty minutes. Only the spray of stars lit the scene that had first been described by Captain Moresby to help all future sailors, 'starboard a rock protruding by as much as 3 feet at low tide, beyond which is clear water'. There was the rock unchanged by over 150 years of erosive water and there beyond the freedom of the open sea.

A course was set to take us way beyond the grip of the reef and then south-west towards the Four Brothers, and as we turned, the cloud cover evaporated to reveal a planetarium, life size and crammed with constellations.

It was a still night, so still that each star could watch its own light reflected in the black mirror of the sea. As each star and planet rose over the horizon it gave the illusion of ships' lights coming to meet the ketch, each pointing out our path with a pencil stripe of silver light.

The night went all too fast and the dawn watch saw the Three Brothers rising in the distance. From five miles out the diminutive bulk of Brother No. 4 came clearly into view, or at least the surf that pounds counter-clockwise around its margin could be easily picked out. The sea was still mirror flat. Surely if we were ever going to be able to land on our new-found island today must be it. Contact was made by radio with the members of the main party who were already hard at work on the transects. All was well and rendezvous was planned for the lee of the new island as soon as the morning dive was complete.

As we approached our objective we sized up the problem; flat calm it might be, but the swell was still breaking against the vertical walls of the island, sending spray clear across its apex. With Mont and a brace of non-submersible cameras to land, plans had to be laid with utmost care. Two inflatables were to be used. One anchored out beyond the breakers was to be the operation platform. From this three strong swimmers took a rope ashore, landing like corks from a bottle high on the rock. The rope was then made fast to a pile of rocks and the second boat, stripped of everything but its buoyancy, was hauled along the rope. It all sounds easy, but with the transport boat shooting up and down 8 feet at the end of the run and with jagged rocks only a few inches away it took some doing. Nevertheless Mont and the cameras were able to step ashore dry shod.

The total area of semi-dry land was no more than 0·55 hectares and consisted of an outer ring of jagged mini-cliffs with a nice sea arch at one point. Inside this was a circlet of coral slabs thrown up by the storms of ages as if to protect the central bowl of the island, which is composed of part sand and part talus.

One end of this natural amphitheatre was covered with a dense, close-cropped vegetation, but the bulk of the area was devoid of life except for the swaying heads of some 400 large black and white birds and about half that number of chicks in various states of fledge. Even from the rim of the island there was no mistaking the fact that we had found the nesting-place of the Blue Faced or Masked Booby, the birds we had seen flying past Eagle on a number of occasions.

In the centre of the island each nesting pair were separated by about 4 feet, so it was possible to walk between them without getting pecked. Around the core of the colony other birds were nesting at about half that density, while around on the cliffs unpaired young adults were just hanging about. The nest sites were completely devoid of nesting material and the residents, both young and old, were very vociferous and complained loudly about the cameras. But here was a chance to photograph every stage in the life-cycle of these rather comic birds, so as they scolded we clicked, although they quite quickly lost some of their fear and settled down to enjoy the attention.

The lack of nesting material certainly was not due to absence of the raw materials, for although the total flora comprised only six species, two of them were present in some abundance. The flora included at least three plants that we had found elsewhere as regular components of the nests of Brown and Red Footed Boobies.

On the edge of the main colony, the sand was full of holes, and a count showed that forty of them were occupied by Wedge-tailed Shearwater chicks. All of these seemed quite friendly, almost as if they were hoping for a snack to break their daily fast. Only four of the burrows contained adults sitting on eggs, and as is the wont of the Shearwater clan, when disturbed they did not fly off but flapped around helplessly until we moved on, when they quickly returned to the nest duty.

A rock ridge separated the Shearwaters from the cliff top itself and the whole length of the ridge consisted of corals fossilised in the position in which they had grown: proof again of another section of raised reef. Most surprising of all however was the fact that on the most exposed side of the islands the 'Cliffs' fell in a series of broad steps, each step occupied by a pool that was almost continuously fed by sea spray. Each pool contained the unmistakable iridescent pink-tipped colonies of the two species of *Pocillopora* growing at least 3 feet above the highest range of the tide.

Just above these elevated living corals was a stretch of mottled coral gravel and as we approached a bird shot off from almost beneath our feet to reveal its egg laid on the open gravel. It was a Black Naped Tern, evidently another bird that cannot be bothered to build a nest. Having described the vegetation and counted all the birds we left the island almost as easily as we came; well, that was until we tried to raise the anchor. The whole section of reef was honeycombed with elongated caves and the 56-pound sinker had plummeted down into the depths of one of these where it had become firmly lodged in a crack. But we were not held up for long. Down went Alan Baldwin and solved the problem all on one breath of air. The sea was crystal clear and it was easy to see him swim down into the cave which was creaking with Spiny Lobster and suggested some fantastic diving to come.

Something was however worrying me, niggling away in my mind: a new island. Great. What more could any expedition want to discover? A new nesting population of Masked Boobies; almost as good, but the more I thought about the Boobies the more I worried. Show me a plant and ninety-nine times out of a hundred I shall remember its name when I meet it again. Now I had met Masked Boobies before and our new discoveries didn't look quite right. However, knowing that I am not very good on birds, I kept my mouth shut and just worried.

17.
The Tower
of Babel

A mile and a quarter south of Eagle Island is Sea Cow, a stepping-stone on the long hop down to Danger Island itself. Sea Cow was going to be the king-pin in the main survey, the aim of which was to ascertain the exact location of the islands in relation to each other. In order to do this we had to be able to get direct sightings between all the members of the group and to be able to link Danger in with this survey we had to get the instruments at least 20 feet above the surface of Sea Cow.

Usually such sites of reference are located on hills or large rocks well above the terrain which is being mapped. In the absence of any hills or other such objects within the vicinity it had been decided to construct a mighty tower, mighty enough to support all the necessary instruments and an operator in the guise of one Dave Young.

The landing on Sea Cow was a hazardous operation at the best of times and a technique akin to that used to get on to Little Brother was always employed. Eight long billets of wood for the tower, together with masses of survey gear, did nothing to help the operation. We were not helped either by the clever remarks of the day's lucky divers, who drove past on their way to their transect, shouting, 'You've got the wood, build a bridge.'

More wood was added to the construction pile from the island flotsam and from the work of the second shore party, whose task was to cut a swathe clear across the island which supported a large stand of broad-leaved trees. Slowly and sometimes not so surely the tripod rose up above the *Scaevola* and *Tournefortia*, eventually to top the local stand of coconuts. The local Red Foots regarded the operations (or was it the operators?) with some measure of disdain, while the Frigates came in to get a close look at what was to be their new vantage-point.

It was a very hot day and someone who shall remain nameless had forgotten the limers, so very soon, constructors, swathers and surveyors alike were beginning to know the real pangs of thirst.

Mont, Warren and I had taken on the job of recording the bird populations and mapping the many features of the shoreline, so we had to tramp around the periphery of the island measuring and counting as we went.

About half-way round dehydration was beginning to get a real hold and with 422 pairs recorded on the census board, our thoughts were much more on the missing limers than the exact number of Boobies. I began to feel quite jealous of the great birds, which appear to have no problems over water supply. Whether they obtain all they need by extraction from their fish diet, or whether, like the Petrels, they can actually drink sea water and get rid of the salt by secretion from special glands, I don't know, and at that point I didn't care. I did know that

The tower of Babel
marks one angle of a
gigantic triangulation.

only on Egmont and Eagle were there any barachois and we had never seen any large birds drinking their waters. Oh, to be beside one of the barachois! I would drink it all, including the hydrogen sulphide.

On we went, the total count reaching a staggering 950 pairs of resident Red Foots, and as we got back to the landing point there was one of the dive parties swimming ashore with a five-gallon can of limers. We all drank deeply and the afternoon's work was completed. The tower was ready for the surveying.

Sea Cow is an interesting island, for although it is close to Eagle, much of its surface is still under broad-leaved forest. Coconuts there certainly are, together with paw paw and *Alocasia*, the giant rhubarb-like plant we had seen on Salomon, but probably owing to the very difficult landing, the island had never been used as a regular source of coconuts.

Despite the depredations of man, especially in the field of paw paw planting, the forested part of the island was resplendent with Takamaka. One of these trees had a girth of four yards and in its shade the paw paws were having a hard time of it. Some had grown up tall and thin to produce a ridiculously small crown of leaves well over 25 feet above ground level. This is no mean feat for a plant which does not produce any real wood. Paw paws are in reality herbs, and they gain their support not from wood but from the phloem or bast, a living tissue whose main function is to transport sugar around the plant.

Much of the island was covered by open stunted vegetation developed on a thin covering of sand over solid coral rock where even the hardy *Scaevola* found it impossible to make a 'living'. This was undoubtedly tern country and the pads were full of 11,500 noisy adult Noddies of the Common variety, sorry, species. In contrast the forest and scrub was the home of the Lesser Noddies and here nesting was in full swing with an estimated population of 800 pairs.

The usual flutter of Fairy Terns came to inspect us whenever we came too close to their nests, but the majority of these were at the top of the trees and, remembering the catastrophe on Egmont, we had almost given up any hope of adding pictures of the nestlings of this most beautiful bird to the annals of the expedition. Luck was however with us, for on one of the survey walks we had seen sitting on a coconut

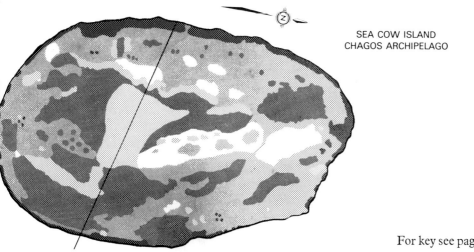

SEA COW ISLAND
CHAGOS ARCHIPELAGO

For key see page 104

bole about 2 feet above the ground a bird which from a distance looked not unlike a piebald Turnstone. Close inspection revealed a short head with a black bill and the almost transparent flight feathers just growing. Their pure whiteness was only masked by a light brown mark on the upper wing that looked more like a watermark than a definite pattern.

The last of the pleasant surprises of the bird life of Sea Cow was a large colony of Wedge-tailed Shearwaters, some of the chicks of which were so fat that they could no longer struggle into the protection of the burrow. Each one of these monster balls of down hid as best as it could beneath the litter of fallen coconut fronds.

Each island we visited provided us with new information concerning the web of life which made such full use of the potential of its dry acres. Our understanding of the relationship between substrata, vegetation and bird life was almost complete.

Wherever the sand was deep enough and especially where it was underlain and interspersed with broken coral rock, this was the domain of the Shearwaters. Here too was the most advantageous place for the growth of the broad-leaved trees. Shearwaters were more often than not birds of the forest floor, and here the roots of the trees helped to bind the sand together, providing excellent conditions for the birds' burrows.

The deepest sand was along the coastal strip, but here the possibility of inundation by storm waves and the lack of sand-binding roots made it unsafe ground for the Shearwaters. The only bird which appeared to use this open sand as a nest site was the Black Naped Tern, laying a single egg directly on to the warm sand. Close behind the open beaches the *Scaevola* and *Tournefortia* grew in profusion, the latter appearing to prosper better on the more rocky outcrops. On all the islands, *Scaevola* appeared to be the commonest of the shrubs, which in some ways is a pity because its fragile branches appear unable to support the weight of nesting Boobies. Out of the many thousands of Booby nests recorded from the Chagos only a very few were on *Scaevola*. Apart from this omission from their nesting repertoire, they would use any type of bush or tree and their nests ranged from just above ground level to the very topmost branches of the canopy. Especially favoured were any trees which stood proud of an expanse of low vegetation. Each one of these choice sites looked like some bizarre Christmas Tree hung with mobile candles, each set in an untidy holder from the edge of which white guano dripped like candle wax on to the lower branches.

The Frigates shared the Red Foots' preference for broad-leaved trees. They however appeared to favour those which were situated close to very tall emergent palms on which the males would sit keeping one eye on the nest and another out to sea for the hapless Boobies.

The Sooty Terns were undoubtedly the kings of the open vegetation which had developed on porous sand, where gravity soon drained away the water supply, and on solid rock outcrops, although they appeared to be restricted to the Three Brothers. On the other islands most numerous were the Common Noddies, who, although they preferred the more shady spots, would use all the open vegetation whenever the need arose.

In contrast the Lesser Noddies always occupied trees and of all the birds only these appeared to have mastered the craft of nest life in the unlikely condominiums of the coconut palms, although in many cases the bases of each palm provided a pad for a couple of their near relatives.

The more specialised breeders like the Bridled Tern and the Brown and Masked Boobies, all of which appeared to require an open pad

Success at last both for
the expedition and the
Fairy Tern, our first
picture chick, click.

The most abundant of
the boobys, Red Foot or
is it Red Feet?

from which to launch out to sea were the real rarities of the islands.
Their success was undoubtedly restricted by their choice of nest site.

There is one species of Booby which is even more restricted in its
habitat and that is the fabulous Abbotts Booby, today known only from
Christmas Island way over in the east of the Indian Ocean. Its chosen
nest site on its only island home is in the branches of stunted trees

where it raises its young at some distance from the sea. You can therefore imagine the excitement when during one of our many trips to Sea Cow, Mont saw what was undoubtedly an Abbotts Booby flying quite low over the sea. Could it be that they are nesting on Danger?

The Tower of Babel was complete and the readings were duly taken, first using a telerometer to measure the distances to fixed points on all the other islands, followed by a theodolite to measure the requisite angles. Even my meagre knowledge of Pythagoras showed me that with this data to hand an accurate map was possible. Our cluster of islands could now be set in their correct position along the edge of the Great Chagos Bank. All we required was a set of star sights to fix the position of Eagle.

It all sounds very easy, but of all the tasks of the expedition this was without doubt the most time-consuming and tedious, but Dave Young bore it all well. The most difficult part was humping the heavy gear from one station to another only to find that the spray misting across the reef flat made measurements impossible. It was even worse if the station was way out on the reef ridge, when the walk turned into a long wade, the waist-deep water hiding loose coral cobbles and deeper pits. Also, once out on the reef ridge, it was easy to see the divers bobbing about in the boats and Dave, though a surveyor by trade, was a diver at heart. Couple all this with long nights of star gazing and long days at the calculating machine and you can understand the loneliness of a long-distance surveyor when dealing with very flat terrain.

The most satisfying aspects of his job, he said, were being able to stand on top of the Tower of Babel and imagine how it would be to fly with the Frigate birds and get a really good look at the land marked on his maps, and in piecing together all his bits of information to give us ground-bound humans a Frigate's eye view of our temporary home.

While all this land survey work was going on the ketch made a rapid dash to Diego Garcia in order to obtain some important stores. During the voyage dives were organised on the far side of the Chagos Bank in order to ascertain the welfare of the reef along the most exposed stretch of its perimeter. The news came back that living corals were present but in most places less than 20 per cent of the reef front was alive.

18.

The Island
Called Danger

The dive programme on Eagle was complete and the news from Gan was good after some major problems which had started with a broken anchor chain. The ketch was ready to transport the B.B.C. camera crew to join us. The planned three weeks in which to make a film was now slashed to a precarious two and that meant that all the other jobs had to be completed before her arrival. The enormous pile of boxes of coral specimens had to be dealt with, re-labelled, wrapped and re-boxed ready for transportation home. The results of the most recent 'grots' were stinking away in the depths of the forest. They had to be cleaned to perfection and packed away with care.

For two days the base camp buzzed with new activity, each person tying up his various tasks before film extra was added to the list of jobs still to be completed. We hadn't yet landed the expedition on Danger, let alone surveyed it.

A sweepstake was organised, one can of beer allowed you to guess-timate the time of first sight of the ketch, winner to take all. A rainy morning reduced visibility so much that the people who had made the earlier selections soon said goodbye to their beer. Finally the cry of the 'Ketch Ahoy!' rang across the island and 'Sharky' collected the jackpot as everyone manned the boats to go out and escort the *Four Friends* to her moorings.

Warren, Mark and Chang and three members of the British Broadcasting Corporation's famous Natural History Unit were on the

A booby trap

deck, the latter pink from fresh exposure to sun and wind.

Now began a race to get the ketch organised, the B.B.C. men their atoll legs and the expedition geared up, all within twenty-four hours, ready to set off to survey the island called Danger.

An overcast sky and driving rain ensured that the secrets of Danger would be kept just a little longer. Although the main party huddled under a sail bag on the foredeck kept their eyes peeled, our first glimpse was not until we were about five miles off. As Danger appeared out of the gloom it didn't look anything special, a mile and a half of rock and sand, the usual plume of Frigates, flights of welcoming Noddies on their way out to feed. Was there any new information which Danger could add to our knowledge of the Chagos Bank?

The historical records certainly indicated that Danger was rarely visited and then only to collect wild coconuts. The name perhaps hinted at the hazards of doing just that; anything might be in store. We selected the lagoonward side of the island, which in the present state of the wind was the lee shore. The landing was almost too perfect and very soon the stores were taken in through a narrow channel to be landed safe on the beach. The cameras whirred as Alan, Mont and myself shook hands, remembering the time, now over two years ago, when we had leant over the rail of the *Stromness* and said that one day we would land on Danger Island.

The rain had gone and the sun shone at about 1000th at F22 and it was very hot. Gallons of limers went in, to emerge almost immediately as small fountains through a whole variety of sweat pores. Unloading and setting up camp was a chore both physically and mentally because the island was there waiting. By 16.00 hours Mont and I were free to begin the land survey.

Red Foot Boobies were everywhere, except on the *Scaevola*, in great profusion. There were in fact a trio of pairs parked right on the edge of the camp site within fat-spitting distance of Harry's galley. Apart from a little bit of their beak-dipping display and some harsh squarking they soon settled down to enjoy our company and seemed completely unperturbed even when the generator was switched on, bathing them in an extra eight hours' light.

The actual survey of the perimeter of the island was going to take two days and eventually it allowed us to state that Danger had more of these birds than any of the other islands, a staggering 4,200 pairs.

The only other animal which we found in great abundance during our first short walk was the Robber Crab. They were everywhere, a fact which seemed somewhat surprising as of all of the islands this had the fewest coconut palms. During our walk we actually witnessed two of these ungainly creatures coming out of the sea back on to dry land; perhaps they were returning after mating. As we trudged round the island in the gathering dusk it is only fair to say that we were a trifle disappointed; the bird life was not as rich as we had hoped. The most peculiar thing was that apart from a few Brown Boobies and a large population of *Gallus gallus var. aerobaticus* there were no ground-nesting birds at all. The completely open patches and expanses of low stunted vegetation were devoid of life apart from a multitude of land crabs. No Sooties and no Noddies, yet in the light of our experience on the other islands the habitat was ideal for them. Had we arrived on Danger at the wrong time of year or did the large population of Robber Crabs play a similar role to the rats on Eagle and Egmont?

Despite its recorded history, Danger had been the habitation of man. Although less than one quarter of the island is covered with palms, much of the rest is pockmarked with the saucer-like depressions in which palms were probably planted but from which they had long since disappeared. The chicken population was also large and it was

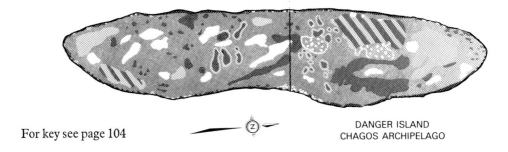

For key see page 104

DANGER ISLAND
CHAGOS ARCHIPELAGO

not unusual to see a 'cackle' of them perched up in a tree, with many broods of chicks rushing about in the undergrowth.

Broad-leaved forest covers about half the island and this includes large stands of paw paw, which yielded some succulent fruits that undoubtedly helped the diet of both the chicks and the crabs.

The forest included among its canopy a mystery tree typified by cabbage-like leaves, a tree which we had found on a number of the other islands. Here for the first time it was in full flower and thus revealed its identity to be *Pisonia grandis*. We collected pollen from the flowers in the hope that we would be able to find similar grains deep down in the peat deposits on Eagle and thus prove that this had been one of the original Big Trees which grew on the islands.

Apart from the forest the main features of Danger were large tracts of land almost devoid of any plants at all. When we had taken our first walk around it was dry and these open areas were indeed deserts with a few scattered tufts of plants dry and lifeless among the black coral rocks.

The weather was however about to take a turn for the worse and unfortunately for our filming schedule the turn was going to last for twenty-four hours, a day and night of strong winds and torrential rain.

This made camp life somewhat unpleasant and under these conditions the expedition members took second place in the dry tent which was part full of camera gear and film stock that had to be kept dry. Our camp was in a small clearing in among the fringe of *Scaevola* and *Tournefortia* and our local trio of Boobies were now so friendly that we had the opportunity of filming the whole of their ungainly nest building and incubation. They were in fact the focal point for camera men both amateur and professional whenever the rain stopped and light allowed. We even managed to watch the whole ritual of the change over of incubators. The female had been patiently sitting guarding her two eggs from the cascade of rain and the seemingly bitter cold wind. In came Dad fresh fed from the sea to begin the head dipping, beak jabbing ceremony; the female responded until one supposes she was satisfied that his intentions were honourably focused on egg minding, when off she went. The male then settled down for what turned out to be a 48-hour stint on the nest.

A well-preened Booby appears to be absolutely weather proof, although even the greatest Booby addict would have to admit that after a few hours in the rain they do look less comfortable. Nevertheless the brooding birds simply snuggled down and brooded even harder.

That night it started to rain at around 18.30 hours just as Mont and I had got to the tip of the island having counted 2,763 Booby nests. We sheltered under a diminutive palm much to the amusement of the local hermit crabbery, the members of which were gathered in their hundreds there in the dry. We waited, to no avail; the rain got heavier and so we started off back to camp.

Supper in the rain, although its usual gastronomic affair, was a somewhat dampening experience with all members huddled beneath a flapping parachute that had been erected to help protect Harry and his cooking from the sun. The prospects of sodden Liar Dice was too much even for the addicts and so for the first time we retired early wet and cold.

From my wet vantage-point in the mouth of tent number one, it was possible to watch the myriad insects that had collected in the shelter of the glowing white canopy. All of a sudden, three Boobies, two young and one adult, flopped down into the light and waddled into the protection of the parachute. There they sat fluffing out their feathers to dry and, going through the whole post-bath preening routine, they settled down for the night dry and contented. The generator coughed, spluttered and as its raucous noise fell into silence the lamps went out. Time to go to sleep.

Exactly what prompted the next move I don't know but all three Boobies suddenly blundered up, tried to take off and flew into tent or, rather, flysheet number two. They landed on various members of the expedition who until that moment had been fast asleep, and as they did

175

they complained loudly about the sudden blackout. Eight sleepy divers and three Boobies in actinic shock all under a very damp flysheet is not the best of combinations, especially as it is the habit of frightened Boobies to regurgitate half-digested fish in all directions in an attempt to lighten their take off payload. Pandemonium reigned until the birds had extracted themselves from the soggy mêlée, returned to their perches and settled down for the night. Peace reigned once more and it kept raining steadily down on the soaking canvas.

Apart from curtailing the film-making the rain did one good thing. It revived all the plants and especially those of the open dry areas. What had only the day before been dry desolation was in the light of early morning an expanse of shining green moss, with patches of lighter green variegated with the white flowers of *Borhavia* and the yellow stars of *Portulaca* and *Sedum*. The scent of the *Scaevola* flowers was overpowering and the palms and the forest were alive with Noddy Terns sheltering in the base of the coconut fronds. Thousands upon thousands of them looked down at us from their perches and as the rainstorm abated they took off to their feeding-grounds beyond the reef. Several counts on a number of mornings and evenings put their population at some 24,000 Common Noddies and 16,000 Lesser Noddies.

The dive programme centred around two main transects, one on the lagoonward side of the island, the other exposed to the open ocean. The contrast was enormous.

The sheltered lagoonward side sloped almost imperceptibly. So gradual was this slope that five miles out from the reef front the echo-sounder on the ketch registered only 90 feet. This was the inner rim of the old atoll and its whole length was protected from the seaward side by the island and from the lagoonward side by the shallow water shown on the Moresby map. An almost unbelievable sight met our underwater eyes, the whole wide flat rim was stiff with coral, a jungle of Stagshorn coral branching as far as one could see in perfect visibility. At first sight it appeared to be a monoculture of only one type of coral. However probing in among the forest of Stagshorn revealed a whole range of genera and growth forms. If any reef in the world deserves the title 'All alive oh!', this must surely be in the running.

All alive oh: Stagshorn coral — what a lovely sight!

Diver and Caranx, or Caranx and diver, depends on which way you look at it.

The B.B.C. on B.I.O.T.

1.

2.

5.

6.

9.

10.

13.

14.

3.

4.

7.

8.

11.

12.

1. *Greater Frigate*
2. *Greater Noddy Tern*
3. *Brown Booby and Nest*
4. *Fairy Tern*
5. *Masked Booby*
6. *Sooty Tern — Fledgling*
7. *Little Green Heron*

8. *Red Footed Booby on Nest*
9. *Greater Noddy Tern*
10. *Lesser Frigate*
11. *Black-Naped Terns*
12. *Lesser Noddy and Nest*
13. *Wedge-Tailed Shearwater*
14. *Bridled Tern*

The exposed side was equally spectacular, a broad reef front sloped to a depth of about 60 feet, and then began to fall away to be lost in the excitement of a 'drop off'. The wealth of corals was perplexing; every sample plot required at least fifteen minutes to probe its diversity to the full. The full panoply of reef life exploded on every side, fish of every pattern and hue, Shark, Barracuda, Grouper were all there and as the coral hammers hammered, the cameras whirred on and captured the whole thing.

Apart from the ring a ding ding full of life reef, the most interesting feature of the seaward edge was a false reef ridge running parallel to the reef front at a depth of about 40 feet below sea level. Both it and its component coral communities were very like the cofferdam reefs we had found on the exposed side of Egmont.

We had done it, saving, as one always should, the best for the last. We had not only proved once again that along the most sheltered section of an atoll the best of the living reefs were to be found but we had recorded the fact on celluloid for all the world to see.

One more main objective only was left and that lay on our path home north towards Eagle Island. Almost half-way between Danger and Sea Cow was Transect No. 24 passing across a very narrow reef channel, christened Passage Jacques in honour of the father of our sport!

Deep down everyone knew that to complete the job we must dive, survey and film this reef channel. The ketch was loaded and off we motored. By the time the ketch was on station it looked a long long way to the nearest dry land and the wind was beginning to pile up the

For key see page 104

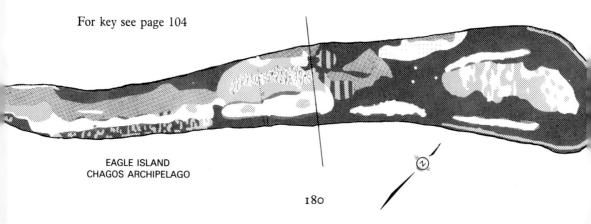

EAGLE ISLAND
CHAGOS ARCHIPELAGO

rollers. Three inflatables were loaded and launched and three dive teams were put down from the boats, which were anchored exactly where the echo-sounder had pinpointed the edge of the channel.

The first team in included Peter Crawford and the underwater camera wielded by Ray Pringle Scott. After their requisite time they surfaced shouting excitedly about big fish but it was our turn next and we didn't wait to listen. I was to go in with Alan Baldwin, Dave Young, Tom Peake and Adrian Lane, Stan Stanley standing by in the dive boat. When our turn came we plummeted over into a somewhat murky sea and headed off down the shot line to the bottom which was at around 60 feet. There were a number of shark motoring about so we mounted a shark guard and checking that the anchor weight was well wedged we started the routine survey. Nothing unusual except a scatter of Black Dendrophyllia – at this depth? – well, we were in a reef channel. Having completed the work the team swam to the edge of the drop off and peered longingly down into the whiteness of the channel proper. If only we had the time! But we hadn't and so we turned reluctantly back to our heap of coral sacks by the anchor. I hadn't finned more than a couple of strokes when I sensed excitement in the water. Turning I saw a knot of three of my buddies all gesticulating at an immense Grouper which had swum up out of the channel. It was gigantic, 500, 1000 or more pounds. I couldn't even start to guess, all I know is that as it swam along behind the three divers they were lost within its fishy compass. It took no notice at all of all our excited interest, swimming slowly past the knot of divers, opening and closing its mouth in a very fishy way. No sooner had this fantastic fish vanished into the gloom than another just as large if not larger swam into view. The second was a Hump Head Wrasse and looked more grotesque and hence much more menacing than the first. Beside these two monsters the flurry of sharks was almost forgotten in the excitement of those few spectacular moments.

We arrived back at the pile of coral sacks ready to ascend the anchor rope but it had gone. We looked around and could see no sign of the 56 lb. sinker; the inflatable had probably dragged its anchor while we were away on the edge of the channel. Collecting the precious sacks we followed the instructions in the dive rule book to the letter. Bunch and

1.

2.

5.

6.

9.

10.

3.

4.

7.

8.

1. *Stachytarpheta jamaicensis*
2. *Canavalia cathartica*
3. *Cordia subcordata*
4. *Portulaca mauritiensis*
5. *Morinda citrifolia*
6. *Carica papaya*
7. *Ipomea pes-capreae*
8. *Tournefortia argentea*
9. *Cocos nucifera*
10. *Hernandia sonora*

The Fourth Brother, christened Resurgent

keep close together during the ascent, then when close to the surface send one man up to look for the boat. We hovered in mid water and Alan Baldwin went up to look for the boat. It all seemed much longer than it actually was, but he rejoined us signalling no boat in sight. Was it just my imagination, or were the sharks behaving in a different way? We bunched closer together and all rose to the surface where we inflated our life-jackets. All that was visible from down at water level were the waves rolling in apparently from every point of the compass. Our dive boat was nowhere to be seen but there between the waves was the top of a mast riding high through the water. Warren Blake was at the cross trees and his sharp eyes picked us out in the mess of water. In next to no time our dive boat was alongside and we heaved ourselves thankfully out of the water. In the time that had elapsed since the start of our dive, conditions had certainly worsened and the gigantic swell, together with a surface current, had whipped our dive boat away and with no point of reference against which to judge their position the boat handlers had been oblivious of the fact. The dive leader decided that conditions were too bad to continue work. Two thunderflashes were exploded underwater, the signal for abort, and the other team surfaced, dragging their coral specimens behind them.

What a place, what a dive and what fish! A fitting end to our expedition, which was now complete bar the shouting.

There was some more diving still to do and we all returned to the Four Brothers to film the expedition at work and the full range of the bird life.

During our revisit to the Fourth Brother we planned to make a special study of the characteristics of that puzzling population of Masked Boobies. Weather conditions and time were however not on our side and so we decided to take a single specimen for examination. An unpaired male from the edge of the colony was selected for the purpose. Study by the experts back in Britain has shown that, although it does have a large beak, all its main distinguishing features lie within the known extremes of variation found within the other Indian Ocean population of Masked Boobies. This finding is certainly in keeping with the hypothesis that the birds have come to the island only since the coconut farmers left the area. All we have found is a new population recently moved in to take up residence. I am however not convinced; a sample of one is not very good on which to base important conclusions. Only a full-scale study of the population carried out *in situ* on their rocky home will tell, and until this has been done I have an open mind.

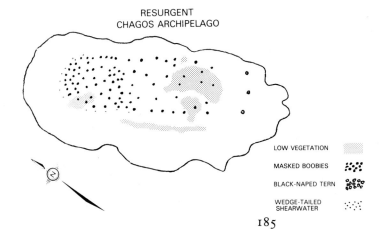

RESURGENT
CHAGOS ARCHIPELAGO

LOW VEGETATION

MASKED BOOBIES

BLACK-NAPED TERN

WEDGE-TAILED
SHEARWATER

Diving included a near incident with an 18-foot Hammerhead Shark which swam past Doc when he wasn't looking, so close that he could have reached out and stroked it. Our return to Little Brother almost drowned Dickie Bird on his way in along the rope and we found all the *Pisonia* trees stripped of their leaves but their branches full of Lesser Noddy nests. Likewise South Brother was full of nesting Sooties, all part of the ever-changing pattern of life which left us with one big question. How many birds actually use the potential of these islands throughout the span of an average year? All this was of course exciting but nothing could quite come up to the earlier experiences of Brother No. 4, the discovery of the peatlands on Eagle, the living reefs off Danger and the great fish of Passage Jacques.

We packed our corals, dismantled the base camp and left the island as clear of evidence of our sojourn as we could. The saddest moment was when the ketch sailed round the R. F. A. *Resurgent* to take her leave back to Egmont, Gan and then the Seychelles. The journey back to Gan was one long party during which we told Captain Butterworth and the crew at least something of our adventures and named Brother No. 4 'Resurgent' as a token of all their hard work both in landing and retrieving those of us who were lucky enough to live one foot in Paradise.

19.
Paradise can be Regained

As I sit at home, far from the midday albedo of a tropic sun thrown back from the pure white of a coral beach, and attempt to write this book it all seems like a hazy dream. Thank goodness for all those copious notes, overflowing data sheets and acres of photographs. Without them the facts could have so easily slipped into the realms of remembered fiction.

It wasn't all a dream; we did discover, survey, experience and record it all.

The Great Chagos Bank is a gigantic coral atoll and its reefs are not dead. Reef-forming (hermatypic) corals are present in abundance and thanks to the help of Zena Dinesen and the knowledge of Dr. Brian Rosen, one of the British Museum experts, we now know that our excited estimates of diversity were not too exaggerated. The coral lists include at least fifty-six genera and sub-genera of hermatypes, not bad for an area thought to be poor in reef-forming corals.

It would appear that the most active reefs of the Bank are situated around and between the extant islands, that is along the western and north-western margins of the atoll where they are sheltered from the main blast of the Trade Winds. The most active coral growth is thus along the most sheltered side of the atoll. This together with the similar findings for Egmont shows that the accepted theory that reefs grow into the prevailing weather is not of universal application.

Much more work is needed on the dynamics of reef growth before an overall set of 'laws' can be formulated, let alone applied. We were lucky, as we had been able to see first hand the structure of three atolls, but that does not mean that our conclusions are of direct application elsewhere.

A coral atoll is a gigantic living community, existing tenuously between the extremes of environment in which its living components find their niche. Too much bad weather will spell doom for any reef, likewise too little turbulence may result in deoxygenation of the reef waters and hence death to the reef-forming corals. Between these extremes lies the whole spectrum of the coral seas and this makes the fascination of being a fully submersible reef ecologist.

The fish populations of the Bank were unfortunately not studied in detail, nevertheless it may be stated that they were rich both in species and in the abundance of large specimens, especially of the predators. This is probably linked to the fact that access to the waters of the Bank is both difficult and dangerous and that the bulk of the fish are absolutely dependent on and restricted to the areas of living reef front, which are practically unfishable by conventional means. The production potential of the area was made manifest by the abundance of fish that had made their home in the artificial reef created by the wreck of the *El Maren*.

Despite the meagre data we have relating to this aspect of the Chagos ecosystem, and in full knowledge of the exaggeration factor in many fishermen's tales, there seems little doubt that the waters of the Bank could support a much larger population of fish-eating birds.

The copra farmers of the past have certainly had an adverse effect on the vegetation of all the islands except Resurgent. Their depredations range from the introduction of a range of exotics to the replacement of large tracts of the natural vegetation by their geometric plantations. However on all the islands the natural vegetation appears to be holding its own and the broad-leaved forest is making a comeback at the expense of the coconuts.

The presence of peat deposits on Eagle Island which are rich in sub-fossil pollen grains is of great importance in that it promises a detailed record of the vegetation which pre-dated the copra farmers.

Of all the feral animals known to have been left on the islands by

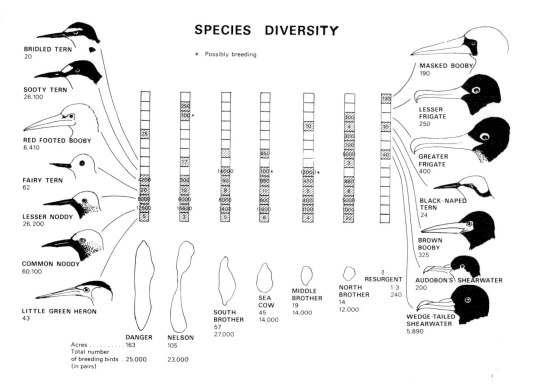

SPECIES DIVERSITY

BRIDLED TERN
20

SOOTY TERN
26,100

RED FOOTED BOOBY
6,410

FAIRY TERN
62

LESSER NODDY
26,200

COMMON NODDY
60,100

LITTLE GREEN HERON
43

* Possibly breeding

MASKED BOOBY
190

LESSER FRIGATE
250

GREATER FRIGATE
400

BLACK-NAPED TERN
24

BROWN BOOBY
325

AUDOBON'S SHEARWATER
200

WEDGE-TAILED SHEARWATER
5,890

DANGER   NELSON   SOUTH BROTHER 57 27,000   SEA COW 45 14,000   MIDDLE BROTHER 19 14,000   NORTH BROTHER 14 12,000   RESURGENT 1·3 240

Acres 163   105
Total number
of breeding birds . 25,000   23,000
(in pairs)

man, today only rats and the domestic hen survive, although only in isolation each from the other. Rats are only present on Eagle and Egmont islands which are devoid of large populations of nesting birds. This is very unfortunate because these two islands make up more than 80 per cent of the total dry land area of the group. In contrast the nest site potential of the remaining 202 hectares is overflowing with bird life, an estimated total of 116,562 pairs made up of populations of fifteen species.

The discovery of all these new nest records in 1975 is in itself surprising, especially when it is remembered that the bulk of these (except those on Nelson) have probably come into existence since the evacuation of the islands in the early 1930s.

From our knowledge of the relationship between the vegetation and the nesting birds it is possible to calculate the approximate number of each type of bird which could move in and take up the nest site potential of Egmont and Eagle, if the rats were removed. The calculations and potentialities are shown in diagrammatic form overleaf.

BIRD ISLANDS

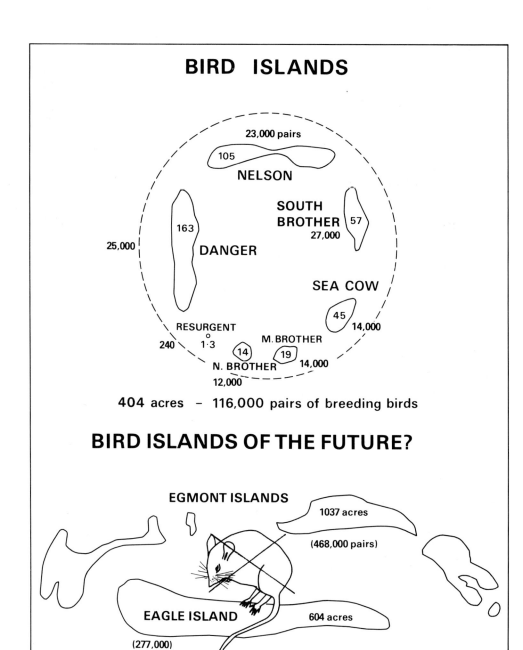

23,000 pairs

105

NELSON

SOUTH
BROTHER 57

27,000

163

25,000

DANGER

SEA COW

45

14,000

RESURGENT

240

1·3

M. BROTHER

14

19

N. BROTHER

14,000

12,000

404 acres – 116,000 pairs of breeding birds

BIRD ISLANDS OF THE FUTURE?

EGMONT ISLANDS

1037 acres

(468,000 pairs)

EAGLE ISLAND

604 acres

(277,000)

Total 2,045 acres – 861,000 pairs of breeding birds

Advice has been and is being sought through the ornithological and scientific literature concerning the wisdom of such an action. Bearing in mind the fact that the rat populations have not been subjected to any artificial control over the past fifty years, if indeed at all, it would seem feasible to effect their eradication using modern rodenticide technology. If this were accomplished it could create one of the best sea bird sanctuaries in the world.

It is therefore suggested that:

(1) The whole of the Chagos Bank, including Egmont Island, is worthy of consideration as a Marine and Terrestrial Nature Reserve of international importance.

(2) Local, regional and international agreement should be sought to that end to ensure its complete protection forever.

(3) Subject to approval of the local and regional government (which is that of the British Indian Ocean Territories or B.I.O.T.) and the world bodies concerned with the conservation of Nature and Natural Resources, the rat populations on both Egmont and Eagle islands are controlled in order to allow the local populations of nesting birds to expand to fill the resource.

(4) A year-long expedition is mounted which will go to the Group, its object being to:

  (a) complete the survey of the Great Chagos Bank, including the reefs and islands of Peros Banhos and the Salomons and the nearby submerged reefs of Blenheim, Victory and Pitt Banks;

  (b) to draw up a comprehensive programme of management and study for the future.

Here is one place in the world where man has fought and has lost his battle for economic survival within the living ecosystem of the area. Here is one place in the world where nature need not be trained to live alongside man. I believe we can control the rat population and aid the recovery of the broad-leaved forest. I know we must plan to have the Great Chagos Bank in its 'natural' state forever.

The royalties derived from the sale of this book will be used to help achieve this objective through the Jubilee Trust of the British Sub Aqua Club.

P.S. *Sula abotti* Ridgeway is the correct Latin name for Abbotts Booby.

It is at present confined as a breeding bird to Christmas Island (Lat. 10°30′S, Long. 105°40′E) in the eastern Indian Ocean. It was once known to nest on Assumption Island but has not attempted to nest there since 1930 owing to gross interference by man. On Christmas Island it nests in tall trees some distance from the sea, and despite sensible and well-enforced laws its numbers are declining. The reasons for this decline are obscure and may be linked with increased human pressure but more likely due to the build-up of the island's Frigate populations. Whatever the exact reason, here is a species in need of new nesting sites.

Its presence around Eagle Island is indeed exciting and there are certainly a number of areas of broad-leaved forest which would appear ideal for the establishment of a new nesting colony. If the rats were controlled it might just be possible that the Abbotts Booby would be able to take up residence before all the nesting real estate was occupied by the more local bird populations.

Like all the Boobies, *Sula abotti* is a delightful bird, it does however have one special quality. When danger approaches it just sits tight on the nest and closes its eyes so that it can't see the danger and therefore does not get too worried. A stupid thing to do? Well, it might be but for the fact that evolution has painted on each eyelid another eye, so that its potential attacker thinks that the brave bird is still looking at him and goes away. If the world loses *Sula abotti* it will be a sadder and duller place, we mustn't let it happen and here is a chance, agreed a long shot, to redress the balance in favour of this fabulous bird.

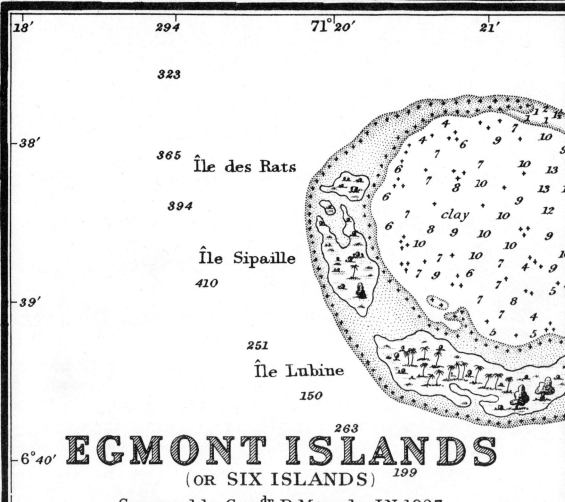

18' 294 71°20' 21'

323

-38' 365 Île des Rats

394

Île Sipaille
410

-39'

251
Île Lubine
150

263
EGMONT ISLANDS
-6°40'
(OR SIX ISLANDS) 199

Surveyed by Com.^dr R.Moresby I.N. 1837
281
With additions and corrections to 1964

Mag.Var.^n 7°35'W.(1974) nearly stationary

NATURAL SCALE 1:72,600 (at Lat 6°39') 493

Projection – Mercator

-41' 19' 71°20' 21'

clay